Robert G. Wilson
25[illegible] N. N[illegible]stle Ave
[illegible] Ill.

Electron and Nuclear Counters

THEORY and USE

BY

SERGE A. KORFF, M.A., PH.D.

Associate Professor of Physics and Supervisor of Physics Research
College of Engineering, New York University

NEW YORK

D. VAN NOSTRAND COMPANY, INC.

250 FOURTH AVENUE

1946

PRINTED IN THE UNITED STATES OF AMERICA

PREFACE

It is the purpose of this book to gather together and summarize the pertinent facts regarding the theory of the discharge mechanism and the practical operation of various types of counters. Although counters have been known for about forty years, they are even today surrounded by an atmosphere of mystery, and their construction and operation are claimed by many competent scientists to involve "magic." Various laboratories have developed special procedures for their manufacture and use, often without knowing why particular techniques appear to be successful.

This book first discusses the internal mechanism of the discharge in the counter. It then presents the constructional and operational features which are desirable, and the best means of securing them. Subjects discussed include the conventional Geiger counters as well as counters for special purposes and those selectively sensitive to particular types of particles, such as those which preferentially count neutrons in the presence of a strong background of gamma radiation.

The first chapter serves to introduce the subject, and to describe the progressive changes in counter behavior as the voltage is raised. The terminology to be used in describing counters is next defined. Then the operation of the instrument, first as an ionization chamber, then as a proportional counter, and finally as a Geiger counter, is developed and the theory and operation of each different type of counter is set forth. The practical aspects are next considered, and the construction of counters is taken up. The reasons for the various constructional features are given. The errors and corrections encountered in using these devices are discussed. Finally, the various electronic circuits, which are the essential auxiliaries to the successful operation of various kinds of counters, are presented.

The book is written on an intermediate level for users of counters, most of whom are persons with scientific training but who do not possess specialized knowledge in the field of Geiger counters. It presupposes an acquaintance with the main concepts of atomic physics, such as ionization, recombination, radiation and diffusion, as well as some familiarity with vacuum tube circuits. It is intended to be of use to graduate students and to the many industrial laboratories and medical research institutions which are finding counters to be useful tools of research.

SERGE A. KORFF

September 1945

ACKNOWLEDGMENT

It is a pleasure to acknowledge the assistance received from many persons not only during the actual work of writing this volume, but more especially during the years while the author was acquiring the background information in this subject. It is probably true that most education is acquired by discussion of various aspects of the problems being studied with colleagues working in this and allied fields. The author was fortunate during the early 1930's in being able to confer about the background material with R. A. Millikan, H. V. Neher and John Strong, and subsequently with M. A. Tuve, L. R. Hafstad and L. F. Curtiss. Later he was equally fortunate in having many stimulating discussions with W. F. G. Swann, W. E. Ramsey, M. E. Rose, C. G. and D. D. Montgomery, G. L. Locher, W. E. Danforth and T. H. Johnson. He is especially indebted to his colleagues at New York University, R. D. Present, H. V. N. Hilberry and J. Simpson. The entire text has been read and checked for errors by Bernard K. Hamermesh. The drawings for the figures were made by Jane K. Hearn. Finally the author wishes to extend his especial thanks to Dr. J. A. Fleming of the Department of Terrestrial Magnetism of the Carnegie Institution of Washington who gave important support to the study of counters at a time, during the early development period, when many persons doubted whether counters could ever be made into reliable and reproducible instruments of scientific measurement.

LIST OF SYMBOLS USED

- A The gas amplification
- B A constant
- C The electrostatic capacity, usually in microfarads
- D The standard deviation
- E The electric field in volts per cm
- F An area in sq cm
- G The efficiency
- I The current, usually in amperes
- L The Loschmidt number, 2.705×10^{19} molecules per cc at STP in a gas
- N Avogadro's number, 6.06×10^{23}
- R The resistance, usually in ohms
- U The volume, usually in cc
- V The potential in volts
- Å Ångstrom unit, 10^{-8} cm

- a The slope of the curve of ionization cross section as a function of energy
- c The velocity of light in vacuo
- d A distance
- e The charge on the electron. *Note:* Where the letter e is followed by an exponential, it is understood to be the base of natural logarithms 2.7183 . . .
- h Planck's constant
- i A flux or number of particles crossing a sq cm area per sec
- k The mobility
- l A length
- m The mass of the electron in grams
- n A number
- p The pressure of a gas, usually in atmospheres
- q The charge, usually in microcoulombs
- r A radius
- s The specific ionization, in ions per cm at STP
- t A time
- v A velocity
- *ev* Electron volt
- Mev Million electron volts
- kev Thousand electron volts

- α The first Townsend coefficient
- β The recombination coefficient
- ϵ An energy
- λ A wavelength
- μ The atomic weight
- ν A frequency
- π 3.14159 . . .
- ρ A density
- σ A cross section, in sq cm

A letter or number with a bar over it designates an average value.

CONTENTS

CHAPTER 1

INTRODUCTION

A. History

Since the early experiments of Rutherford and Geiger, made nearly 40 years ago, it has been known that a useful device capable of counting individual atomic particles could be made by a combination of two electrodes in a gas. The device will detect the passage of charged particles through the volume between the electrodes and manifest this passage in the form of an electrical impulse. The apparatus will thus count the particles and is therefore called a *counter*. Counters have a wide variety of designs and uses. Almost anything can be made to count. One well known laboratory has an exhibit which consists of a fork and a spoon supported in air with a potential difference between them. This arrangement provides counting action and is a good, if somewhat extreme, illustration of the point that virtually any disposition of electrodes and gases can be used for the purpose. This situation has led to the publication of a great number of quasi-empirical papers, in which the several authors report that the particular combinations of gases and electrodes used will count. Unfortunately, these observations have generally been made in an unsystematic manner, with few controlled conditions, and are hence of little value, and sometimes quite misleading.

The problem of making counters into instruments of precision and of causing them to count quantitatively and accurately and to yield reproducible results is in no way insoluble, providing the basic factors are recognized. A great deal of work by a large number of investigators has been done on the problems pertaining to the construction and operation of these devices, and many theories regarding the functioning of counters have been evolved.

As early as 1908, Rutherford and Geiger [R1] arranged a cylinder and axial wire, applied a potential, and projected particles into the cylinder. They found that "the current through the gas due to the entrance of an alpha particle into the detecting vessel was magnified . . . sufficiently to give a marked deflection to the needle of an electrometer of moderate sensibility." They had devised the first counter, making use of the additional ionization produced by collision, as the electrons produced by the alpha particle traveled toward the central wire, to give an increase in the pulse size by a factor of "several thousand." Cylindrical symmetry in the distribution of the electric field was used from the first, and shortly thereafter Geiger's [G1] point counter, which employed spherical geometry, was developed. For some time, various types of filar electrometers [G2] were used to detect the pulses. These types were superseded as the rapid development of vacuum tubes during the two decades from 1920–1940 made electronic circuits possible which were faster, easier to adjust, readily portable and capable of amplifying the pulses as well as recording them. Counters with large sensitive areas were constructed in 1928 by Geiger and Mueller [G3] and have been generally called Geiger-Mueller counters.

The observation that at certain voltages the counter would detect alpha particles only, while at higher voltages it would detect both alphas and betas, was made in the early experiments. Later developments by Geiger and Klemperer [G4] in 1928 laid the foundation for the modern technique of "proportional counting" in which the difference in the ionization produced by an alpha and a beta particle is made the basis for distinguishing between them. Thus, proportional counters have been known about as long as any counters, although they were not so designated until much later.

vated substances may be followed through complex chemical and mechanical transformations, the location of lost tubes of radium, the detection of minute radioactive impurities, and the testing of samples of radioactive ores. In the study of petroleum geology, counters have found a use. A counter and a source of radiation may be lowered into an oil well boring, and the counter will measure the different amounts of radiation scattered back to it from the various strata of different materials through which the bore passes. This procedure can be made to reveal the location of hydrocarbon deposits, and the technique is in wide use today.

Neutron counters, being sensitive to neutrons, which in turn are strongly scattered by hydrogen-containing substances, have been used to detect the presence of hydrocarbon accumulations in the ground, or in pipes or other containers. An absolute altimeter has been proposed, in which the scattered neutrons would indicate water nearby, and the technique may be used for locating water.

In short, any industrial use of nuclear physics may be aided by using these instruments in the detecting procedures. It will be recalled that in metallurgy, diffusion phenomena, order-disorder studies, and tracer researches have made use of artificially activated substances. In each case, counters represent a useful detecting technique. Similarly in chemistry, the study of reaction rates, surface properties, molecular structure, low vapor pressures, equilibrium measurements, small solubilities, and catalysis have all been aided by the use of artificially radioactive elements. In each case a counter could be used to detect the activity, both in amount and in nature, and could follow the active substance through various changes and reactions. In geology, in addition to prospecting for radioactive deposits, identification of minerals, and assaying, counters have been employed in connection with artificially activated substances used in sedimentation studies.

It is the purpose of this book to describe the properties and behavior of counters and counting systems, and hence we next turn to a discussion of the electrical phenomena produced by counters.

C. Description of the Phenomena as a Function of Voltage

1. Low Voltage Region. Let us consider any system of the type ordinarily used for counting action, such as a cylindrical cathode and an axial wire anode. It is evident that the main function of the cylinder is to distribute the potential, and to form a volume in which the electric field is defined by the geometry of the electrodes. Suppose the wire of this system is connected to a sensitive device for measuring the voltage changes, or pulses which may appear on it, such as an oscilloscope with high amplification; let us consider the pulse sizes and distributions as the voltage across the counter is raised.

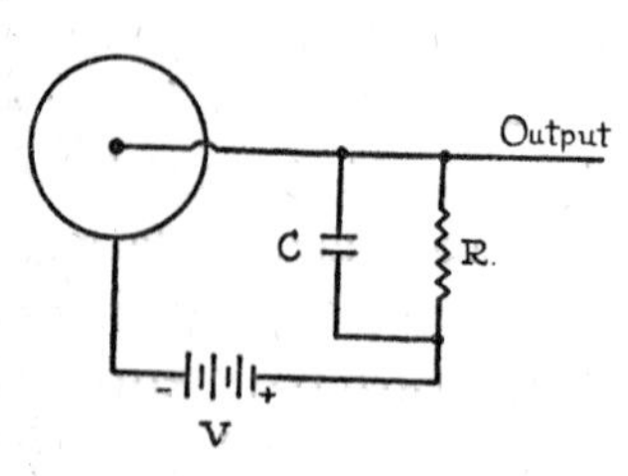

Fig. 1–1. Fundamental counter circuit.

Such a counter will then form a part of the fundamental circuit shown in Fig. 1–1, in which the cross section of a counter is depicted, a potential is applied across it, and a resistance R inserted in order that a pulse may be passed to the detecting unit. The condenser C is understood to include all the distributed capacity in the circuit. The recovery of the wire after a pulse has occurred is controlled by the familiar exponential RC time constant and cannot be made shorter than this value but can, of course, exceed this figure if the discharge conditions are suitably varied. We shall assume that curves of the number of counts at various voltages are obtained, while the flux of radiation passing through the counter is kept constant. We shall consider the wire to be positive with respect to the cylinder and shall therefore discuss the collection of negative ions and electrons on the central wire. The operation of the counter in various voltage regions will be described. We shall show how this device functions at low voltages as an ionization chamber. As the voltage is progressively raised, the device becomes in turn a proportional counter and a Geiger counter. We thus have several voltage regions: the low voltage region, the proportional region, and the Geiger region, in which quite different types of phenomena occur, and in which the same counter may be used for quite diverse purposes. We shall consider these in turn.

The word "ionization" is used in physics in two distinct senses. In the narrow sense it means the process of removal of an electron from a neutral atom. We shall use it in its broader sense, to mean any act or process by which a molecule or atom which was neutral acquires a charge, or by which electrons are freed in a gas. We shall also use the word to describe the results of the process, in the sense that we may say that "ionization has been produced in the gas." We are less concerned with the nature of the event causing the ionization, and more interested in the collection of the charges produced and in all the processes which accompany this collection. The reader will recognize that we must therefore discuss electrical discharges in a gas. Since this book cannot also be a treatise on gas discharges, we shall assume some acquaintance with the subject and refer the reader to standard texts for further details. We shall now examine the results which follow when ionization is produced in a counter.

It will be recalled that when ionization is produced, in general an ion-pair, positive and negative, is formed from what was initially a neutral atom. We must consider what happens to both of these fractions as they are drawn, respectively, to the negative and positive electrodes. For the sake of simplicity we shall discuss these two parts separately, but it must always be kept in mind that both are present and that their interactions must be considered.

At zero voltage across the counter, there will be no fluctuations in the potential of the central wire, save those caused by the random arrival of individual ions on the wire. If a small voltage is applied, a field is established in the space between the cathode and anode, and any positive ions formed in this volume tend to drift toward the cylinder, and the negatives toward the wire. As the voltage is first applied on the cylinder, the arrangement becomes in effect an ionization chamber in which any electrons produced in the volume of the counter are swept by the field to the central wire where they are collected. The size of the voltage pulse appearing on the central wire is determined by the number of charges arriving and by the distributed capacity of the central wire and anything attached electrically to it, such as the grid of the tube in the first stage of the amplifier. The wire potential will also be subject to a transient influence if a positive space charge exists. A change in potential, dV, will be produced by the arrival of a charge, dq, on an electrode of capacity C. In terms of the arrival of particles of unit electronic charge equal to 1.60×10^{-19} coulombs, the rise in potential of the central wire will be given by

$$dV = dq/C = 1.60 \times 10^{-7} n/C \qquad (1\text{–}1)$$

where n is the number of electrons arriving, dV is the rise in potential in volts, and C is in micromicrofarads. Eq. (1–1) assumes no effect of positive space charge and hence is correct *after* the positives have been collected. The changes in potential of the wire, while the positives are moving out to the cylinder, will be discussed later.

The time rate of change of the voltage is determined by the rapidity with which the ions are collected on the central wire, providing this is small compared to the time constant RC. To know this, we must know the mobility of the charged particles collected, which for negative ions is of the order of 1.2 to 1.4 cm per sec per volt per cm referred to air at standard temperature and pressure. For electrons, the mobilities are much greater and the drift velocity is larger by a factor of 1000 to 10,000. Thus, for example, in a counter of 1-cm radius with 1000 volts between the electrodes and 1 atm. pressure, the collection of negative ions would take place in approximately 10^{-3} sec, whereas electrons will all be collected in a microsecond or less. In an ionizing event, electrons and positive ions are formed. The probability of the attachment of these electrons to neutral molecules to form negative ions will be discussed later. It will suffice here to say that in most cases few negative ions are formed, and we shall therefore mention chiefly electrons here.

At low voltages V_o, the electrons do not create any additional ions by collision during the collection process. The number which arrive on the central wire will therefore be equal to the number which were produced in the initial ionizing event less the number which have disappeared by recombination. The number which disappear by recombination will be small in most counters, since the fields are high and the pressures are low. The size of the pulse which arrives on the central wire is independent of the collecting voltage as long as the field is sufficient to cause ions to move with an appreciable velocity and remains independent of the potential as the voltage is increased up to the point at which secondary electrons are produced by collision in the gas.

The positive ions, in the meantime, travel outward to the cylinder where they are neutralized. Later we shall discuss this process in detail; for the time being, it will suffice to assume that they are collected at the cylinder and thus disappear.

2. The Proportional Region. When the voltage across the counter is raised above that minimum V_p, at which secondary electrons are first formed by collision, the pulse which appears on the wire will then be larger by reason of the additional ions formed by collision. This process, as the potential is slowly raised, will first take place in the immediate neighborhood of the wire where the field is greatest. It will take place as soon as the field, dV/dr, is sufficient so that the incoming electron attains enough energy to produce ionization upon its next impact. The electron loses most of its kinetic energy each time it collides with an atom. Hence, if it is to produce ionization by collision, it must gain an amount of energy sufficient to ionize, i.e., equal to the ionization potential of the gas, in one free path, between collisions. The original electron and the new one thus produced will each be accelerated again by the field and will produce still more ions by collision. This process is cumulative, and an "avalanche" of electrons is thus produced. The phenomenon is frequently called the Townsend avalanche, in honor of J. S. Townsend who, forty years ago, did important pioneer work in this subject. We thus may define r_o, the critical radius, as the radius at which the field is sufficient so that the process of cumulative ionization starts. The lowest voltage at which cumulative ionization is observed is defined as the threshold voltage V_p for proportional counter action.

If there are A ion-pairs formed by collision as each electron travels toward the central wire, then the size of the voltage pulse on the central wire will be given by a modification of eq. (1–1), namely

$$dV = 1.60 \times 10^{-7} An/C \qquad (1\text{–}2)$$

The quantity A is defined as the "gas amplification." This number may in actual practice vary between the limits of unity, in the case when the counter acts like an ionization chamber, to about 10^7 at the end of the proportional region. In general, a counter ceases to be in the proportional region when the figure exceeds 10^7, but in many cases a counter cannot be operated in the proportional region when values of A exceed about 10^3. The useful limits on A depend on the type of gas. The theory describing the dependence of A on the gas in the counter, the voltage, the geometry and other factors will be discussed fully in Chapter 3 in the section on proportional counters. As long as A remains a constant, the counter will produce a pulse dV which is proportional to the number of ions n formed in the initial ionizing event.

We have already noted that for a proportional counter A does not ordinarily exceed about 10^7. As the voltage across the counter is still further increased, the value of A appropriate to small pulses will not always remain the same as that for A appropriate to large pulses. Thus, for example, if ten ion-pairs were formed in the counter and A were 10^7, the pulse size would correspond to the arrival of 10^8 particles. If, however, 10^4 ion-pairs should be produced in the counter by an initial ionizing event, say, for example, the passage of an alpha particle through the gas, then application of the same A would give a pulse resulting from the arrival of 10^{12} ion-pairs. This, however, is not generally observed. The size of the pulse is frequently limited to about 10^9 ions, and the effective value of A is therefore about 10^5 in this case. It will thus be seen that at higher voltages the value of A is a function of the pulse size. The voltage region in which A is constant is called the "proportional region." The voltage region in which A depends somewhat on the pulse size is called the region of "limited proportionality." It should be noted that counters may be operated in the region of limited proportionality and may still in this region distinguish between the arrival of a beta ray and an alpha particle since there is a large difference in the total number of ions produced by each of these two entities.

3. The Geiger Region. As the voltage is further raised, the dependence of A upon pulse size becomes more pronounced. The counter will enter a voltage region in which the size of the pulse arriving on the wire is independent of the number of ions formed in the initial ionizing event. This is called the Geiger region and is characterized, when viewed on an oscilloscope screen, by all the pulses appearing to be of the same height.

The minimum voltage at which this condition is realized is called the threshold voltage V_G for Geiger counting action. The absolute size of the pulses observed in the Geiger region is, of course, a function of the voltage applied to the counter and will therefore go through a considerable range as the voltage is changed. In the earliest experiments, counters were operated both in the proportional region and in the Geiger region. The transition between these regions is not abrupt. There is a continuous gradation of pulse size as the voltage is raised.

To illustrate the above discussion, let us consider the history of a pulse produced by the passage through a counter of a fast cosmic ray which leaves behind it perhaps 30 ion-pairs, and also the pulse due to the passage of an alpha particle through the counter leaving behind it 10^4 ion-pairs. We shall consider what happens to these pulses as the voltage on the counter is raised (see Fig. 1–2). While the device is operating as an ionization chamber, the pulse produced by the cosmic ray and that produced by the alpha particle will each be collected on the central wire and the magnitude of each will be given by eq. (1–1). The pulse sizes will be in the ratio 30:10,000, and this ratio will be independent of the collecting voltage. As the voltage across the counter is raised, the threshold for proportional counting action is reached. The two pulses will then each increase in size since, as the counter enters the proportional region, the gas amplification A will be an increasing function of the voltage. In the proportional region, the pulse observed on the wire due to the alpha particle will still be about 300 times as large as that due to the cosmic ray. This ratio will be maintained until the region of limited proportionality is entered. As this region is first approached, the value of A appropriate to the alpha particle pulse will cease to increase as fast with voltage as does that appropriate to the smaller pulse. At a slightly higher voltage, therefore, the pulse due to the alpha particle will be less than 300 times as large as that due to the cosmic ray. As the voltage is still further raised and the region of limited proportionality traversed, the ratio of the pulse sizes approaches unity, while the absolute magnitude of each of the pulses still increases as the voltage is raised. The voltage at which the pulse size due to the cosmic ray has become equal to that due to the alpha particle is the Geiger threshold, and above this voltage the ratio of the pulse sizes will be unity.

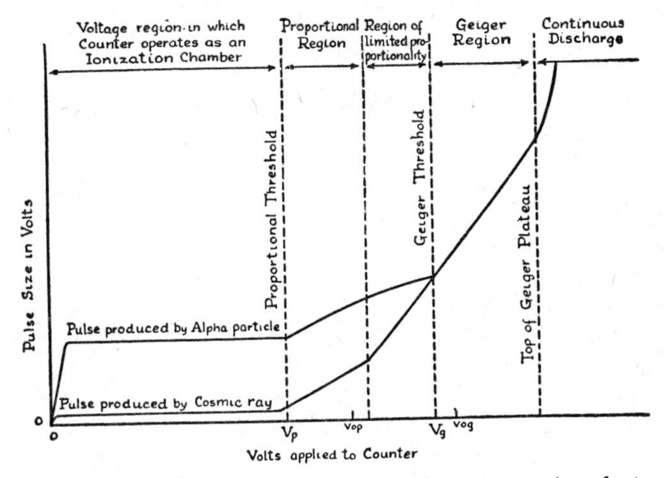

FIG. 1–2. Operating characteristics of a counter in various regions for large and small ionizing events. Top curve shows pulse resulting from passage of alpha particle producing 10,000 ions during its passage through the counter. Bottom curve, pulse resulting from cosmic ray producing 30 ions. The curves merge at the Geiger threshold. Recommended operating voltages: for proportional counting, Vop, near top of proportional region, to get large pulses; Vog, for Geiger counting near Geiger threshold to avoid excessive pulse size and damage to counter.

The absolute magnitude of the pulse will increase with voltage throughout the Geiger region. The dependence will be discussed in the section on Geiger counters. Fig. 1–2, originally given by Montgomery and Montgomery [M1], shows the several regions and traces the pulse size in each.

At the end of the Geiger region, the counter goes into what is called a continuous discharge. This discharge is not really continuous, but consists of a large number of multiple pulses.

The properties of such a pseudo-continuous discharge are not within the scope of this work, and will therefore not be discussed, except to say that a "continuous" discharge constitutes the upper limit of the region of Geiger counting action. Indeed, the growth of multiple pulses is also a gradual phenomenon, and the top limit of the Geiger region is therefore not sharply defined. The curves and complete discussion of this will be given in the appropriate sections. The gas amplification A becomes very large (often $>10^8$) in a continuous discharge. This statement is not strictly accurate if a continuous discharge is considered from a microscopic viewpoint, but it provides an operationally adequate description.

D. Definition of Terms and Symbols to Be Used

For purposes of standardizing the terminology used in describing counters, a series of definitions of many of the important features is set forth below. These definitions have not always been adhered to by all authors, and there is a wide divergence in the literature in the usage of the terms. The definitions described below are those which are in common use at the present time, and while by no means perfect or complete, at least provide a working basis for the terminology of this subject.

Ionization. The act or the result of any process by which a neutral atom or molecule acquires a charge of either sign, or by which electrons are liberated.

Radiation. Electromagnetic or corpuscular radiation being detected.

Ionizing Event. Any event in which ionization is produced, such as the passage of a charged particle through the counter.

Primary Ionizing Event. The ionizing event which initiates the count.

Pulse. A change in voltage of the central wire system of the counter. This change in voltage is usually abrupt and is a result of the collection of ions produced in the gas of the counter.

The Characteristic Curve of a Counter. The curve of the counting rate against voltage, all pulses counted being greater than a certain minimum size, determined by the sensitivity of the detecting circuit.

Plateau. The more or less horizontal portion of the curve of counting rate as a function of voltages.

Operating Voltage. The voltage at which a counter is operated. This is the voltage across the counter measured between the cathode and anode. Symbol V_o.

Starting Potential. The voltage which must be applied to a counter to cause it to count, with the particular recording circuit which may be attached. This potential is not necessarily the same as, and indeed is, in general, not equal to the Geiger threshold. Experimentally, this potential is that at the foot of the "plateau" curve of a Geiger counter and has often been called the "threshold" in the literature. As we shall show below, no fundamental significance can be attached to the starting potential as it is a function of the detecting circuit. Symbol V_s.

Threshold Voltage for Geiger Counting Action. The lowest voltage at which all pulses produced in the counter by any ionizing event are of the same size, regardless of the size of the primary ionizing event. Symbol V_G.

Overvoltage. The difference in voltage between the operating potential and the threshold for Geiger counting action. (Overvoltage $= V_o - V_G$.)

The Gas Amplification in a Counter. The number of additional ions produced by each electron produced in the primary ionizing event as it travels to the central wire. Symbol A.

The Proportional Region. The part of the characteristic curve of pulse size versus voltage in which the pulse size is proportional to the number of ions formed in the initial ionizing event. In this region, A is constant for all pulses at any one voltage.

The Region of Limited Proportionality. The part of the characteristic curve of pulse size versus voltage in which A depends on the number of ions produced in the initial ionizing event, and also on the voltage.

The Geiger Region. The part of the characteristic curve of pulse size versus voltage in which the pulse size is independent of the number of ions produced in the initial ionizing event.

Overshooting. A counter is said to overshoot if the change in potential of the wire is greater than the overvoltage.

Efficiency. The efficiency of a counter is defined as the probability that a count will take place when the entity to be detected enters the counter.

Spurious Counts. A spurious count is one which is caused by any agency whatever other than the entity which it is desired to detect, or the normal contamination or cosmic-ray background.

Dead Time. The time interval, after recording a count, that the counter is completely insensitive and does not detect other ionizing events occurring inside it.

Recovery Time. The time interval, after recording a count, before the pulses produced by the next ionizing event in the counter are of full size.

Resolving Time. The minimum time interval between counts that can be detected. The word may refer to an electronic circuit, to a mechanical recording device, or to a counter.

Time Lag (Statistical). The time between the occurrence of the primary ionizing event and the occurrence of the count in the counter.

Life (Time) of a Counter. The life or life time of a counter is the number of counts which that counter is capable of detecting before becoming useless due to internal failure for any reason (e.g., gas decomposition or wire pitting, etc.). The life is not a time but a measure of the amount of use.

Quenching. The process of terminating the discharge in a counter. A quenching circuit is a circuit which causes the discharge to cease, and the term "selfquenching" as applied to counters refers to those in which the discharge ceases due to an internal (atomic) mechanism within the counter.

Avalanche. If an ion produces another ion by collision and the new and original ions produce still others by further collisions, an avalanche of ions (or electrons) is said to have been produced. The terms "cumulative ionization" and "cascade" are also used to describe this process.

Predissociation. Ordinarily an atom, or simple molecule, if it absorbs radiation, and is not immediately involved in a collision, will lose the absorbed energy by reradiation. A complex molecule (four or more atoms) will usually predissociate before it has an opportunity to radiate.

Cross Section. The cross section of an atom or molecule, usually expressed as an area in square centimeters, is the area obscured by that particle. The cross section of a process (e.g., a collision cross section or capture cross section) is a measure of the probability that that process will occur. The term is usually used in referring to interactions which may occur when one entity moves through a space containing others. Thus, if an electron advances through a gas, the collision cross section of an atom of the gas for such electronic collisions is the number of collisions per atom that the electron will make in a 1-cm advance. Symbol σ. If there are L atoms per cc, the electron mentioned will make $L\sigma$ collisions per cm advance.

CHAPTER 2

IONIZATION CHAMBERS

A. Introduction

In this chapter, we shall discuss the operation of ionization measuring devices in the first or lowest voltage region. In this region the ionization produced in the vessel is directly collected and measured, with no gas amplification. Eq. (1–1) applies, since A is equal to unity. The electrical diagram which applies is that shown in Fig. 1–1. The ionization to be measured takes place inside the vessel. A potential difference applied across the counter causes the ions to be swept toward the electrode and collected on it. The arrival of the ions produces a change dV in the potential of the electrode, as given in eq. (1–1). The problem in the operation of these instruments is therefore that of detecting, measuring and recording the pulse dV thus produced.

There are two distinct types of ionization chambers which accomplish this purpose in quite different manners. In the first instrument the pulses due to the individual particles are detected, while in the second the pulses are allowed to add up, and the integrated total of all the ionization produced in a certain time is determined. In principle the same chamber can perform either function, and which it will perform is determined by the time constant RC of the circuit (Fig. 1–1). If the initial potential of the collecting electrode were V_o, it would have a potential V, after a time t given by

$$V = V_o e^{-t/RC} \qquad (2\text{–}1)$$

Thus the return to $1/e$ of its original value for a typical chamber, with resistance R of 10^8 ohms and capacity C of 10^{-11}

farads, takes place in 10^{-3} seconds. The collection of the ions must take place in less than this time, since if the charge leaks off the collecting electrode through R as fast as it arrives, the rise in potential is negligible. The collection time depends on the mobility of the ions collected, which in turn depends on the nature and sign of the ions, and the nature and pressure of the gas employed in the vessel as well as the field.

In the integrating types of ionization chambers, the resistance R is high, of the order of 10^{15} ohms or so. For the collecting system cited, the time constant is, therefore, 10^4 sec, and a moderately low collecting field is possible. In this case it is necessary to measure the changes in potential of the electrode at suitable intervals. Thus the former type of chamber measures and counts the individual rays whereas the latter type measures the flux or total radiation. In the former type, the recorded pulse size is proportional to the amount of ionization liberated in each primary ionizing event, whereas in the latter, it is not possible to tell, except with the aid of subsidiary measurements, whether a given amount of ionization is produced by a few large ionizing events or many small ones. The decision as to which of these two to use will therefore depend on the particular problems to be studied. We will consider the counting and integrating types in turn.

B. Counting Chambers

Let us consider the aspects of producing and detecting a pulse dV due to an ionizing event which has taken place in the chamber. Such an ionizing event might be the passage of an alpha particle, a beta particle or a cosmic ray, through the chamber. Since an alpha particle has a range of only a few cm in air, it will, in general, expend its entire range in the gas of the chamber. As alpha particles observed in chambers usually come from contamination (usually radium A), we may assume that the alpha particle produces about 3.5 Mev of energy in ionization. Since it requires about 35 volts to produce an ion-pair, a total of 10^5 ions will be formed by the average alpha particle. Provisionally we will neglect recombination. Since the electronic charge is 1.6×10^{-19} coulombs, we have a dQ of 1.6×10^{-14} coulombs, which on a capacity of 10^{-11} farads will produce a pulse dV of 1.6×10^{-3} volts. A beta particle will produce a much smaller amount of ionization and may liberate 10^3 or so ions on its traversal of the chamber, while a cosmic ray passing along a 10-cm path in atmospheric air will produce some 300 ions. If we wish to study cosmic rays, the problem is to detect pulses of 10^{-3} to 10^{-5} volts amplitude. In general, it is practical to detect such pulses only if they take place in a comparatively short time, since most amplifying systems involve measurements of dV/dt. The electrical circuits for detecting such pulses will be discussed in a later chapter.

Let us further assume that the resistance R is 10^{10} ohms, so that a time of 10^{-1} seconds is available. The collection of charges produced in the ionizing event must be completed in this time. Referring to the mobilities mentioned above, if we have a chamber of 10 cm radius, operating at 1000 volts, with average fields of about 100 volts per cm the ionic velocities would be about 100 cm per sec and ions would travel the dimensions of the chamber in 10^{-1} sec.

The speed with which ions may be collected depends on the velocity with which they drift through the gas in the direction of the field. We will define the mobility k of the ion as

$$v = kE/p \tag{2–2}$$

where v is the velocity, E the field and p the pressure in atmospheres. The mobility k is expressed in units of cm per sec per volt per cm for a unit pressure of one atmosphere. Thus we assume that the drift velocity varies directly with the field and inversely as the pressure. Mobilities of both positive and negative ions in various gases have been studied by Loeb and others [L1]. Typical mobilities have been found for positive ions, in air at STP in a unit field (1 volt per cm), to be 1.35 cm per sec, and for negative ions 1.5 for moist to 1.8 for dry air. The experiments also show that the mobilities vary inversely as the pressure except at very low pressures, where the ion experiences few kinetic collisions and has long mean free paths. In hydrogen, the mobility is higher, values around 6 cm per sec being observed.

Electrons will, in general, have much faster drift velocities. Hence they will be collected more rapidly. The average drift velocity n of an electron of charge e and mass m in a gas composed of molecules of mass M is given by the relation $n = (m/8M)^{1/4}(eEl/m)^{1/2}$ where E is the field and l the mean free path. The derivation of this equation will be found in the standard texts on gas discharges. The fast collection of electrons is of considerable importance in counters, since negative ions seldom occur. At the higher pressures and lower fields in ionization chambers, the formation of negative ions is more probable and must be considered. The procedures for computing the number of negative ions to be expected in various gases are described below.

Not all the ions formed in the primary event will be collected. Some of the charges will recombine to form neutral molecules. Recombination may take place when a positive and a negative ion come together without too much kinetic energy. If two ions are allowed to fall toward one another in free space, they would ordinarily not recombine, for under inverse square attractive forces they would acquire hyperbolic velocities relative to one another. We must, therefore, assume that their approach velocities are reduced by collisions with other molecules as they approach one another, or that the recombination takes place at a surface which acts as the third body.

The recombination coefficient β is defined by the relation

$$-dN_1/dt = \beta N_1 N_2 = -dN_2/dt \qquad (2\text{–}3)$$

where N_1 and N_2 are the numbers of positive and negative ions per cc respectively and $-dN_1/dt$ is the rate at which the ions of type 1 disappear. Usually, N_1 and N_2 will be equal. The values of the recombination coefficient have been measured and have been found to be of the order of 1 to 2×10^{-6} for positive and negative ions in air and other common gases recombining in the absence of any appreciable field. It will be noticed that this is about 10,000 times greater than the figure one would obtain by assuming that each ordinary kinetic theory collision resulted in recombination. The fields surrounding the ions thus accelerate recombination due to their electrostatic attraction.

Recombination of free electrons with positive ions is a much less probable process. Kenty [K1] and others have measured the recombination coefficient applicable in the case of 0.4 volt electrons and argon ions and find values of about 2×10^{-10}, a figure which is less than the kinetic collision rate.

Regarding the problem from a geometrical point of view, recombination may be classified as volume, preferential or columnar. The above discussion applies to volume recombination. Preferential recombination may take place immediately after the ion-pair is formed, if the components are not separated quickly enough by the field or are deflected back toward one another by collisions with other molecules. When the ions are formed along a column, as in the case of the dense ionization produced along the track of an alpha particle, some additional recombination may take place before the ions have left the dense track. Columnar recombination has been studied by Kanne [K2] and others, who found that the effective values of beta were increased. Since the speed with which the ions move away from one another in a field would depend on the orientation of such a column in the field, the magnitude of columnar recombination in an ionization chamber will depend on the directions of the paths, and therefore only average values can be assigned.

We may compute the mean lifetime t of the ion before it recombines by the relation:

$$t = 1/\beta N \qquad (2\text{–}4)$$

If the collection time is short compared to the mean lifetime, we shall collect most of the ions before many have been lost through recombination. The mean life of an ion in air at STP has been measured by Hess [H1] and others and has been found to be of the order of 300 sec. This value would be consistent with a β of 2×10^{-6} and an N of 1.6×10^3 ion-pairs per cc. Consequently, a collection time of less than a minute would insure that the loss due to recombination would be small. Consider, also, a chamber such as might be used in cosmic-ray work, having a collecting field of about 30 volts per cm. If such a chamber were filled to 30 atm pressure, the average velocity of the ions would be about 1 cm per sec, and for a 10 cm path, 10 sec would be required for complete collection. Now in such a chamber, N would be 30 times as great as it is for a volume of gas at 1 atm, and consequently if β remained at 2×10^{-6} and N were 3×10^4 (a reasonable figure for cosmic rays at sea level), t would be about 10 sec. We would, therefore, expect that the effects of recombination would be important, as is found to be the case. In counters and low-pressure chambers, however, most of the ions will be collected. Our action in neglecting recombination in counters is therefore justified in the first approximation.

Any ionization chamber will exhibit a certain background, and it is the statistical fluctuations in this background which set the fundamental limit to the smallest amount of ionization detectable in each instrument. This background is caused by three types of radiation: (a) alpha particle contamination of the inside of the chamber, (b) cosmic radiation, and (c) natural radioactivity of the surroundings. The alpha particle contamination may be reduced to a low value by painting the inside of the chamber with carbon black or other very pure organic chemicals such as collodion. A good chamber will still have perhaps 10^{-4} alpha particles per square cm per minute. In some chambers, a gauze has been arranged just inside the surface of the chamber, and charged to a positive potential, which would repel any alpha particles approaching it and drive them back to the walls. However, the front surface of such a gauze will itself emit some particles, and it will be impossible to reduce the background to zero. The number emitted in any given counter will, moreover, be constant, and may readily be counted and thus allowed for. The number of alpha particles will not depend on the pressure of the gas in the chamber, except to the extent that the gas is contaminated with radon, which for carefully purified gases is negligible.

The contribution due to cosmic radiation may be reduced to small value by operating the chamber in a deep mine, but as this is often impractical, it is again desirable to determine the number and allow for it. A rough rule is that about 1.5 cosmic rays per minute will cross every square cm of horizontal cross sectional area at or near sea level. The number is larger at higher elevations, being roughly 3 at 5000 feet and 6 at 15,000 feet. If alpha particles or protons are being measured, these will produce a large amount of ionization compared to the individual cosmic rays, and hence can be distinguished by making pulse-size measurements. Such pulse-size measurements will serve to eliminate the effects of beta rays and gamma rays from whatever source and cosmic rays, except in the integrating type of ionization chamber. In the pulse-detecting chambers, the pulse size will increase with the pressure of the gas in the vessel, but of course the number of cosmic rays and contamination rays will remain constant.

The contributions due to the natural contamination from the surroundings external to the chamber can be reduced by making the walls of the chamber thick enough to exclude these radiations. Thus, for example, in the conventional cosmic ray meters, operating under ten cm lead shields, the contribution due to this cause is negligible.

The final limit to the smallest amount of ionization detectable will be that which can just be distinguished from the fluctuations in the background. In Chapter 5 we will discuss in detail the computation of these quantities. To a first approximation a "square root rule" may be applied. For example, a chamber exhibiting a background of ten alpha rays per minute may be used to measure intensities of as low as three alphas per minute; and similarly for the normal cosmic ray and beta ray background at sea level.

The shape and size of the chamber is usually determined by the nature and number of particles to be detected. Thus, for example, a chamber designed to count alpha particles may be made quite small, thus reducing the background due both to cosmic rays and to contamination. A suitable window through which the particles to be measured may be projected into the chamber must be provided. This should be no larger than necessary, both for reasons of mechanical strength and also because such a window is also transparent to contamination radiation originating nearby. The body of the chamber, or the sensitive volume, need not be larger than the range of alpha particles in the gas which it contains. For alpha particles, this will ordinarily not exceed a few cm. For higher energy protons, however, the range may be large compared to the dimensions of the chamber, since, for example, a 10 Mev proton has a range of about 1 meter of air. Hence, in detecting protons, only a small fraction of its range will be expended in traversing the chamber.

Typical arrangements of electrodes in chambers, suitable for detecting alpha particles or protons, are shown in Fig. 2–1. A differential chamber may be constructed as shown in Fig. 2–2, by placing the collecting electrode in the middle of the field, so that positive ions are collected on one side and negatives on the other. Then, a particle which passes right through the chamber will produce substantially equal numbers of particles on each side of the foil and the resulting pulse will be small, whereas one stopping in the front part of the chamber will produce ions of which those of one sign only are collected and hence produce a large pulse.

A chamber designed to detect slow neutrons will, in general, be larger in size. Such a chamber may be lined with boron or a boron compound and filled with some gas such as argon, or it may be filled with BF_3 and not lined. In either case, the neutron may be captured by the B^{10} nucleus, in which case an alpha particle is given out. It is these alpha particles which are counted. Since the efficiencies, that is, the ratio of the number of neutrons traversing the chamber to the number de-

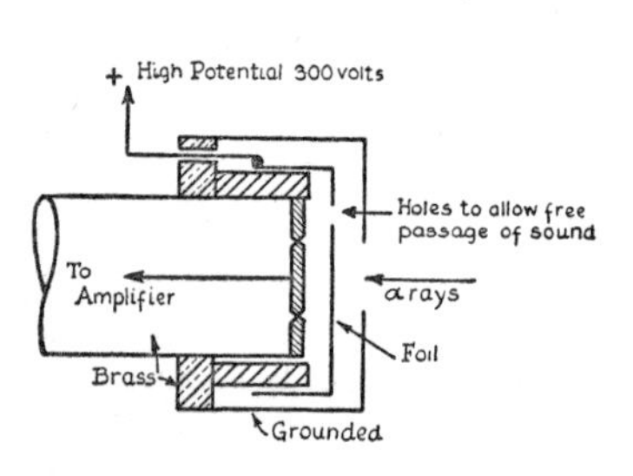

FIG. 2–1. Ionization chamber for counting alpha rays. (W. B. Lewis, *Electrical Counting*, p. 8, 1942)

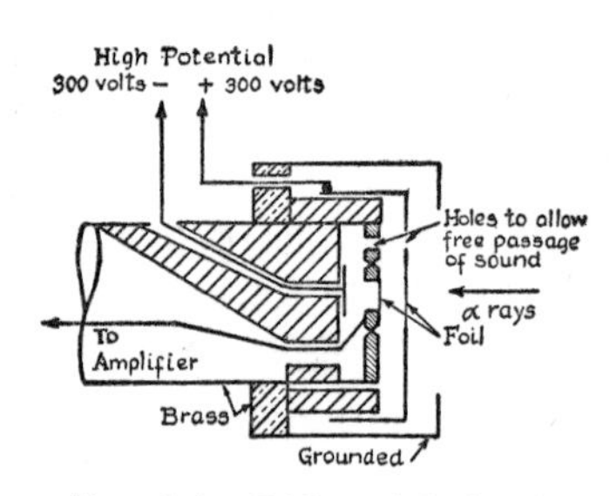

FIG. 2–2. Differential chamber. (W. B. Lewis, *Electrical Counting*, p. 10, 1942)

tected, of such chambers are in general low, it is usual to make the chamber as large as may be convenient in order to secure large counting rates. Such boron-lined or BF_3-filled chambers have been used by various observers and are standard in many laboratories.

Fast neutrons are generally detected by the recoil protons which they can produce. Thus, in constructing ionization chambers to detect fast neutrons, it is usual to dispose some hydrogenous material such as paraffin inside or outside the chamber. Since the range of protons is greater than that of alpha particles, such recoil protons may readily pass through windows which are at the same time strong enough mechanically to sustain pressure differentials and yet not too absorbent. A one or two mil aluminum foil has the stopping-power of a few cm of air; and while it would reduce the range of alpha particles by an amount rendering them undetectable, for protons it presents no serious obstacle. The principal problem encountered with thin aluminum foils is their likelihood of having pinholes. When the pressure differential which they are required to support is negligible, a few coats of lacquer will seal such holes adequately. For higher pressure differences, thicker foils of substances such as nickel-silver are suitable. A 3-mil foil of this material will withstand a pressure of several atmospheres over an area of several square cm, and yet will be the equivalent of only some 50 cm of air; quite enough to exclude alpha particles, but not enough to prevent the admission of a 10 Mev proton. The discussion of the efficiency as a function of the neutron velocity of various types of detectors is given in the section of neutron counting in the chapter on proportional counters.

Ionization chambers are often sensitive to "microphonic" disturbances. These effects are often traceable to the fact that if parts of the chamber move relatively to one another, the capacity of the system changes. If the charge on the collecting electrode is constant, and the capacity varies, the result will be a varying potential or, in other words, a pulse. The changes need not be large. If the capacity of such a system is 10^{-11} farads, and the collecting potential is 300 volts, the charge Q will be 3×10^{-3} microcoulombs. Now if the charge remains constant, and the capacity changes by one part in a million, the voltage pulse will be of the order of 10^{-4} volt. This pulse is of the same order as that produced by an alpha particle. Microphonics may be reduced by increasing the capacity or decreasing the sweeping potentials, but both of these procedures are undesirable since they reduce the pulse size or collection time. Consequently the practical approach to the problem is to construct the chambers with rigidly mounted parts, to provide holes for the equalization of gas pressures inside the chamber, and to mount the chambers on vibration-free supports and surround them with rubber or other sound-absorbing material.

Ionization chambers frequently employ a "guard ring." This ring surrounds part of the collecting electrode, and performs several extremely important functions. A typical arrangement may be seen in Fig. 2–3. The guard ring is often operated at ground potential. Any surface leakage currents across or volume leakage through the insulating material separating the outer shell or case from the collecting electrode, as well as the fluctuations due to the polarization of the dielectric in the high fields will terminate at the guard ring. The poten-

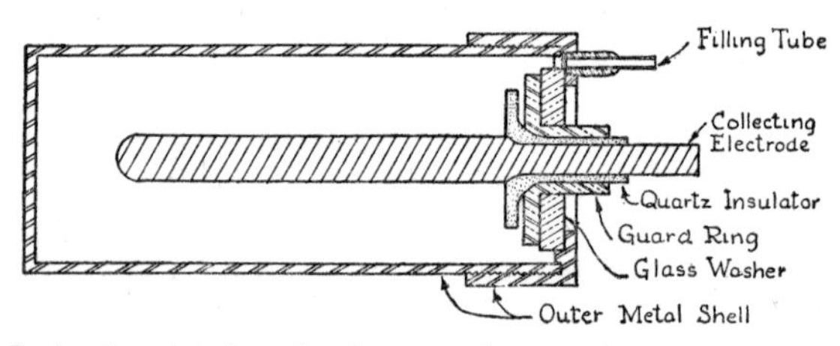

FIG. 2–3. Ionization chamber showing use of guard ring. The surfaces in contact may be sealed with a thin layer of hot wax.

tial difference between the guard ring and the collecting electrode should be small. In case the guard ring is not operated at ground potential, it should be connected to ground through a large condenser, so that its potential will stay as constant as possible. The second, and perhaps the most important, function of the guard ring is to serve as an electrostatic shield and to prevent any part of the collecting electrode from "seeing" any external point or object, the potential of which is not constant. With alternating current supplied to most laboratories today, any part of the collecting electrode system unshielded from the laboratory room may readily pick up pulses of the order of 10^{-4} volts in amplitude. Thus, for example, an ordinary electric lamp operating on AC can readily be detected at considerable distances due to the pulses which it emits. Therefore the geometry of the collecting electrode, the outside case and the guard ring must always be so disposed that no straight line from any point on the collecting system to any point outside the shell of the chamber can be so drawn that it is not intercepted by the guard ring, even though this line passes through considerable thicknesses of the insulating material separating the electrode from the case.

C. Integrating Types of Ionization Chambers

This type of chamber is characterized by the fact that its time constant RC is long compared to the time for the collection of the ions formed in the primary acts of ionization. As the ions from the various ionizing events are collected, the collecting electrode experiences a progressive change in potential. The potential is measured at suitable intervals, and thus indicates the total charge Q collected during the interval.

One type of integrating ionization chamber is compensated. In this type, a second chamber is provided, connected in parallel with the first, but with potentials reversed. This second chamber is small in volume compared to the first, so that the ionization produced by its background will be small compared to that in the main chamber. It is provided with a source of ionizing radiation of some type, usually some uranium on an adjustable rod, which can be so altered in position that the amount of ionization which it produces in the compensating chamber can be adjusted. The entire arrangement is then so balanced that the ionization received in the main chamber is exactly equal to that produced in the compensating chamber. Hence the potential of the collecting electrode does not vary. This type of device, then, is a null instrument, indicating zero under normal conditions, and showing departures from zero, both increasing and decreasing, as the ionization through the main vessel is made larger or smaller than that in the compensating chamber.

Examples of these ionization chambers are the cosmic ray meters designed by Millikan, Compton and their collaborators. In the Millikan instrument,[M2] a built-in electroscope is employed, which consists of a gold-plated quartz fibre arrangement under torsion. When the electroscope system is charged, the fibre is repelled by, and stands away from, its support. Then, as the central system including the electroscope is charged with respect to the case, any ionization produced in the device is collected on the central system. This arrival of charge partly neutralizes the initial charge on the system, and permits the torsional force to cause the needle (the quartz fibre) to approach the support more closely. The position of the needle is a measure of the charge Q on the system, and the change in its position therefore registers the amount of ionization produced in the vessel. It remains, therefore, only to calibrate the device, so that the position of the needle may be quantitatively related to the ionization produced in the chamber, determine the zero and contributions due to natural contamination in the chamber, and then automatically to photograph the position of the needle. The same clockwork mechanism which drives the photographic film also operates a recharging switch and returns the electroscope system to its fully charged position at any desired interval.

The Compton type of meter [C1] is of the compensating type, using a balance chamber with a uranium source which is adjusted until it balances out the normal cosmic radiation. The fluctuations of the cosmic ray intensity above and below the normal averages will, therefore, show on the collecting system, which is connected to a Lindemann electrometer. As with the Millikan type of meter, the collecting system is automatically recharged at intervals and the readings of the electrometer are automatically recorded photographically. Since the intensity of the ionization in the compensating chamber may be altered by adjusting a shield over the uranium source, the zero is conveniently variable, and the device can be set to indicate the ionization produced by the cosmic rays at various elevations. Similarly the ionization produced by any other radiation reaching the interior of the vessel may be measured.

The limit to the sensitivity of these integrating devices is again imposed by the fluctuations in the background. The absolute value of the background can be determined and allowed for, but the statistical fluctuations in this value constitute the ultimate limiting factor.

Both the instruments described above employ a main vessel in which the ionization is detected, filled with 30 to 50 atm of very pure argon. The amount of ionization measured is the total formed along the paths of all the particles passing through the chamber. In the case of cosmic radiation, the specific ionization of the particles is practically uniform along their paths, and virtually no particles end their range in the gas of the chamber. The total amount of charge Q due to ionization produced per particle is therefore given by

$$Q = ne = slpe \tag{2-5}$$

where n is the total number of ions formed, s is the specific ionization in ions/cm/atm for cosmic ray particles in argon, l is the average path length through the chamber, p is the pressure in atmospheres of the argon in the vessel and e is the charge per ion. The chamber is spherical in shape. It can readily be shown that the average path through a sphere is ⅔ the diameter. Hence, the number of ions i formed per particle, in a sphere of 15 cm diameter, l being thus 10, for a pressure p of 50 atm and a specific ionization of 50 ions per cm per atm is 25,000 ions. The change dQ in charge of the collecting electrode is $2.5 \times 1.6 \times 10^{-15}$ coulombs; and assuming the capacity of the system to be 10^{-11} farads, the change in potential is about 4×10^{-4} volt. Since some 300 cosmic rays per minute will pass through such a vessel at sea level, the potential of the collecting electrode changes at the rate of perhaps 0.1 volt per minute, an easily measurable quantity.

The total amount of ionization, appearing in a chamber of the integrating type, in a given length of time is sometimes re-

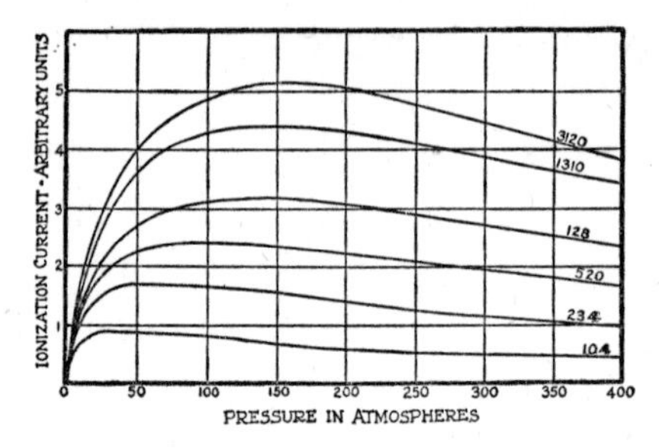

FIG. 2–4. The variation with pressure of the ionization current in air-filled chamber under constant irradiation by gamma rays. Parallel plate electrodes provided uniform collecting fields which are given in volts per centimeter by the numbers attached to each curve. (H. A. Erickson, *Phys. Rev.* **27**, 473 (1908))

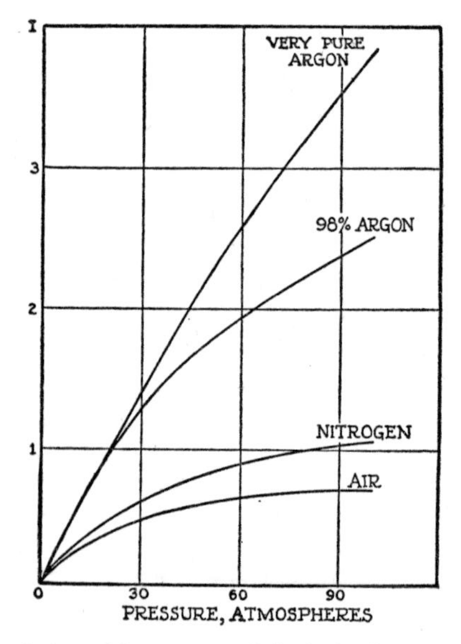

FIG. 2–5. The variation with pressure of the ionization current in various gases, showing the effect of impurities in the case of argon. Ordinate: ionization current in arbitrary units. Abscissae: pressure in atmospheres. (Compton, Wollan, and Bennett, *Rev. Sci. Inst.* **5**, 415 (1934))

ferred to as the ionization current. This conforms to the conventional notation

$$I = dQ/dt \tag{2–6}$$

where the current I in amperes is considered as a time rate of flow of charge Q. From eq. (2–5) it is seen that Q depends on the pressure and it may, therefore, be assumed that in order to have large currents it would be desirable to have high pressures. This is indeed the case at pressures up to that at which the phenomenon of saturation begins to be manifest. At the higher pressures, mobilities become less and the chances of recombination become greater. Fig. 2–4 shows the effects of saturation setting in at various pressures and voltages. At still higher pressures the ionization currents actually decrease due to recombination. Consequently it is not desirable to operate ionization chambers at excessive pressures.

The ionization current also depends on the purity of the gas in the vessel. Fig. 2–5 shows typical curves for the ionization current in argon as the purity of the gas is varied. It will be observed that purity is especially important at high pressures and not especially significant at the lower concentrations.

CHAPTER 3

PROPORTIONAL COUNTERS

A. Introduction

In this chapter we shall discuss the operation of counters in the proportional region. According to the definition previously given, this is the region which has for its lower limit the lowest voltage at which gas amplification takes place, and for its upper limit the Geiger threshold. The upper part of this region includes the region of limited proportionality.

As we have indicated above, the size of the pulse V in volts appearing on the central wire system is given by eq. (1–1), namely

$$V = Ane/C \tag{3–1}$$

where A is the gas amplification, n is the number of electrons formed in the initial ionizing event. If the pulse size V is to be expressed in volts, then e is the charge on the electron in microcoulombs and C is the distributed capacity of the central wire system in microfarads. Eq. (3–1) assumes that the positive ions have been collected and the space charge is absent.* As each initial electron enters the region of high field near the central wire, it will gain enough energy to produce additional ions by collision, and the new electrons thus produced may in turn produce others. Thus an avalanche or cascade of electrons is produced by each initial electron. The gas amplification A is defined as the number of additional electrons pro-

* The transient changes in wire potential while the positive ions are moving out to the cylinder play an important rôle in quenching the counter discharge and will be discussed in Chapter 4.

duced by each initial electron and by its progeny as it travels from the place where it is originally formed to the central wire. Thus A is a measure of the size of the "avalanche" which each initial electron starts, and the avalanches are assumed to be independent of each other. The quantity A is equal to unity in the region below the threshold for proportional counter action, and it becomes very large above the Geiger threshold. In this chapter we shall discuss the determination of the gas amplification A, and the experiments which establish the dependence of A on various factors.

The primary purpose of a proportional counter is to provide a device which will give an output pulse produced by some initial ionizing event of sufficient size to operate a recording mechanism. It is further necessary that some other ionizing event, smaller than this first one by a known amount, shall not produce a pulse large enough to record. This exclusion is essential if pulses are to be studied in the presence of a considerable background of smaller pulses, such as those due to alphas in the presence of those produced by betas, or those due to protons or other nuclear particles accelerated by a cyclotron in the presence of the enormous gamma ray background produced by the same device.

It is evident that any pulse may be amplified to a desired size either in the counter itself (by controlling A) or in the attached vacuum tube circuit. Two independent variables are provided in this manner. We shall discuss the practical limits to counter amplification in this chapter and electronic amplifiers in Chapter 7. In general, only a certain amount of amplification is possible in proportional counters. If we seek to make A greater than a certain value (often about 10^4) the counter becomes a Geiger counter and loses its power of discrimination between pulse sizes. However, the amplification readily obtainable is enough to permit initially quite small ionizing events to be, for example, displayed and studied on an oscilloscope screen.

B. Theory of Proportional Counter Action [R3]

1. Development of the Theory. Consider an electron which has been formed at some place within the volume of the counter by an initial ionizing event. This electron will drift toward the central wire under the influence of the field due to the applied voltage. As the electron drifts in, it will make collisions with the atoms and molecules of the gas with which the counter is filled. Since the counter has cylindrical geometry, the field varies inversely as the first power of the radius. Since the field increases toward the central wire, the electron will acquire more energy per unit path near the central wire. We may also assume that the collisions are, at least in part, not elastic, and that the electron loses most, if not all, of its energy at each collision. When the electron gains enough energy in one free path between collisions to produce ionization, the next time it hits an atom it will ionize that atom. We have thus the beginning of the process of cumulative ionization, which is the basis of counter action. If this collision resulting in ionization takes place at some distance from the central wire, we will then have the initial electron plus the new electron. Both start on their next free paths toward the central wire. Since the field increases nearer the wire, any electron which has acquired enough energy to produce ionization by collision at one point, will acquire enough energy to ionize in each subsequent mean free path.

This situation determines at once the threshold voltage for proportional counter action. This voltage is that at which the electron acquires just sufficient energy to ionize in the last free path before it is collected on the central wire. If the voltage applied to the counter is increased, the critical distance at which ionization commences, will move out into the volume of the counter. As the electron begins to ionize at points progressively further out, the total number of electrons produced will increase rapidly, and we have the beginning of the familiar

Townsend avalanche. If we denote by alpha the number of ion-pairs formed by an electron in each centimeter of drift toward the central wire, we get

$$dN = \alpha N\, dx$$

where dN is the number of new electrons formed by N electrons in this process, in a distance between x and $x + dx$. The quantity α is called the first Townsend coefficient and is a function of the field strength, the nature of the gas and the pressure of the gas. If α is independent of x we may integrate this equation and obtain

$$N = N_0 e^{\alpha x} \tag{3–2}$$

where the constant of integration N_0 is the initial number of electrons. The values of α appropriate to a wide variety of gas discharge problems, for various gases, field strengths and pressures have been measured by many observers, and the dependence of this quantity on various factors is discussed in detail in treatises on gas discharges.[L1, C2, D1] It will suffice to say that Townsend has found an empirical expression

$$\alpha = Ape^{(-Bp/E)} \tag{3–3}$$

where A and B are constants determined by the particular experiment, E is the field and p the pressure. The values of A and B for many different gases have been determined.

We shall now apply this theory to the problem of a counter. In this case we have the field varying inversely as the first power of the radius, and for any given condition we can then compute the number of electrons arriving at the central wire. But first we shall discuss positive ions, which also have a part in the Townsend theory.

Each time an ionizing collision takes place a positive ion is formed as well as an electron. These positive ions drift outward toward the cylinder, and we shall discuss in a later section the rôle which they play when they reach the cylinder.

Since the field through which they travel is decreasing as they advance, they do not contribute appreciably to the cumulative ionization process. Because they travel slowly compared to the electrons, they are left behind as the electrons travel in toward the central wire. The entire electron avalanche is completed before the positive ions have moved any appreciable distance. As we shall see below, the presence of these positives produces a space charge which alters the field in this vicinity, and it is this lowering of the field which is in the main responsible for the counter discharge ceasing. However, in the action of a proportional counter, these effects are not important, and we will assume that we may neglect the positive ions and their effects in the present discussion.

We must now make some further simplifying assumptions regarding the nature of the discharge. We will assume first that recombination does not take place to any appreciable extent. If the electrons or positive ions were to disappear through recombination, the picture would be substantially altered. However, at the low pressures and high field strengths found in counters, recombination is extremely improbable, and our assumption that none occurs is substantially correct. In the chapter on Geiger counters we shall justify this assumption by citing numerical values of the recombination coefficient.

Electron attachment to form negative ions occurs only in strongly electro-negative gases such as oxygen, chlorine or fluorine. The effects found with these gases are discussed in detail in a subsequent chapter. Naturally the production of negative ions would substantially alter the avalanche, and indeed the whole character of the discharge. Negative ions move very slowly compared to the electrons. The importance of negative ions in special cases is also further discussed in the chapter on Geiger counters and the numerical value of the electron attachment coefficient is given. We exclude counters containing electronegative gases from this discussion. We shall assume that the electron avalanche is the only agency by which negative charge reaches the central wire, and that no appreciable number of negative ions is formed.

We shall also neglect fluctuations. This assumption is equivalent to saying that the ionization produced along the path of any electron is equal to the average ionization produced by that electron. Due to statistical fluctuations, any individual electron may of course produce more or less than this amount of ionization. The process of taking this into account in a rigorous discussion would be quite cumbersome mathematically. The fact that we obtain good agreement between experiments and a theory neglecting fluctuations shows that we are not seriously in error when we assume that fluctuations may be disregarded and averages used.

We will assume that the photons, if any, formed in the avalanche do not play any important rôle. We shall find later that this assumption breaks down under certain conditions, and there is evidence that the photons are important in certain cases. Where they are present, the ionization will increase more rapidly owing to their presence and the pulses obtained will be larger. We shall see, however, that photon emission may be neglected in many cases, particularly in those in which complex molecules are present. Secondary electron emission due to recombination and positive ion bombardment of the cathode is also neglected. The agreement between theory and experiment justifies these simplifying assumptions.

We shall next consider the formation of an electron avalanche. In the case of a counter, we have two concentric cylindrical electrodes, the cathode and the central wire. Let the wire radius be r_1, the inner radius of the cathode be r_2, and let a voltage V be applied to the counter. Then the field E at any radius r within the volume of the counter ($r_1 < r < r_2$) will be given by

$$E = V/r \log(r_2/r_1) \tag{3-4}$$

As the voltage across the counter is slowly raised, a value is attained at which the multiplicative process we have called the avalanche starts. The lowest voltage at which this occurs we call the threshold voltage for proportional counter action, V_p. The physical significance of this voltage lies in the fact that it is the minimum at which an electron traveling toward the central wire acquires energy enough to ionize in its last free path before it reaches the wire. We define the radius r_o as that radius at which the avalanche starts. At the threshold r_o equals the wire radius, or $r_o = r_1$. Now r_o in the region of proportional counting never becomes much greater than r_1 (see discussion of mean free paths below), and we may therefore assume an approximately linear dependence on the potential. Hence we may relate the radius r_o, at which the avalanche starts when the voltage applied is V, to the threshold voltage V_p by the relation

$$r_o = r_1 V / V_p \tag{3-5}$$

Thus r_o is defined in terms of the directly measurable voltages and wire radius.

The amplification factor A, defined following eq. (3–1), is determined by the number of ionizing collisions which the electron makes as it travels to the wire, or in other words by eq. (3–2). If we start with a single electron,

$$A = e^{\int \alpha \, dx} \tag{3-6}$$

The number of ionizing collisions depends on the mean free path, which is in turn a function of the energy.

We shall next consider how the mean free path for ionization depends on the energy. This dependence has been studied by a number of investigators.[C2] They find that, in the low voltage region, the ionization cross section increases linearly with the energy. The term cross section is used to mean that area, in square cm, which when multiplied by the number of atoms per cc gives the reciprocal of the mean free path; and the "mean free path for ionization" means the average distance an electron must travel, in this gas, before it makes an ionizing collision. In the higher energy ranges, the dependence is by no means linear, and complicated curves have been found experimentally in many cases. However, we are not concerned here with this extension. In the average counter the mean free path is of the order of 10^{-3} cm. A multiplication or amplification of a factor of 1000 can occur if the electron starts to ionize about ten mean free paths from the wire. Hence these avalanches only occupy the last tenth of a millimeter of space next to the wire. The electron travels through almost the entire dimensions of the counter before it acquires a velocity corresponding to the ionization potential of about 15 electron volts. As the electron approaches still more closely to the wire, it receives more acceleration but it loses energy with each collision. Consideration of eq. (3–4) shows that it does not acquire energy in the last tenth of a millimeter differing by orders of magnitude from that which it received in the previous tenth. We may assume that electron energies involved do not ordinarily exceed 30 to 50 volts. In this energy region, experiments show that the ionization cross section varies linearly with the energy. We may therefore write for the cross section σ,

$$\sigma = a\epsilon - B \tag{3–7}$$

where ϵ is the energy and a the constant of proportionality, or rate of increase of cross section with energy, and B is a constant which does not concern this discussion. This quantity a has been measured by various workers and a few illustrative values are given in Table 3–1.

Since the mean free paths possess various orientations, we must consider an average energy ϵ_{av}.

If we have N atoms or molecules per unit volume, we may relate ϵ_{av} to α, the reciprocal of the mean free path for ionization, through the equation

$$\alpha = N\sigma = aN\epsilon_{av} - BN \tag{3–8a}$$

and we now have the problem of determining the average energy ϵ_{av}.

TABLE 3-1. RATE OF INCREASE OF THE IONIZATION CROSS SECTION WITH ENERGY

Gas	$a(10^{17}$ Cm^2/Volt)	Reference
A	1.81	*
Ne	0.14	*
He	0.11	*
H_2	0.46	†
O_2	0.66	†
N_2	0.70	†
NO	0.74	†
CO	0.83	†
C_2H_2	1.91	†
CH_4	1.24	‡

* P. T. Smith, *Phys. Rev.* **36**, 1293 (1930).
† J. T. Tate and P. T. Smith, *Phys. Rev.* **30**, 270 (1932).
‡ A. L. Hughes and E. Klein, *Phys. Rev.* **23**, 450 (1924).

This quantity can only be determined by making approximations. A rigorous treatment appears to involve considerable mathematical complexity. If we write $N(r)$ for the number of electrons at a distance r from the center of the wire, and $n(\epsilon, r)$ as the number having energies between ϵ and $\epsilon + d\epsilon$, then the change in N as r decreases by dr would be given by

$$-dN = N(r)dr \int_0^{\epsilon_{max}} \frac{n(\epsilon, r)}{l(\epsilon)} d\epsilon \qquad (3\text{–}8b)$$

where $l(\epsilon)$ is the mean free path which is also a function of the energy, and ϵ_{max} is the maximum energy which the electrons have at r, in excess of the average ionization potential of the gas or mixture in the counter. Up to the present time, an exact solution of this integral equation and a determination of the distribution functions has not been accomplished. Certain approximations, however, appear to yield results which are useful experimentally.

First we recall that $n(\epsilon, r)$ has the dimensions of $(\text{energy})^{-1}$ and hence can be written quite generally as

$$n(\epsilon, r) = (1/\epsilon_{av})\phi(\epsilon/\epsilon_{av}) \qquad (3\text{–}8c)$$

where ϕ is a dimensionless function and the dependence on r is contained in $\epsilon_{av}(r)$. We now consider cases where the number of electrons is greatest. Since, of the electrons at r, more than half were formed in the last mean free path, and since the more remote the point of origin, or the greater the energy, the fewer the number of corresponding electrons, the energy distribution will be monotonically decreasing with the most important energy region at $\epsilon = o$. We may thus set $\epsilon = o$ and $-d\epsilon/dr = CV/r$, where $\frac{1}{2}C$ is the capacity per unit length of the counter. Hence from eqs. (3–8a), (3–8b) and (3–8c) a value for the average energy is obtained,

$$\epsilon_{av}(r) = (\phi(o)CV/aNr)^{\frac{1}{2}} \qquad (3\text{–}9)$$

where $\phi(o)$ is the number of slowest electrons, a quantity which we normalize and take as unity in the discussion which follows. Hence, combining with eq. (3–8a) we have

$$\alpha = (aNcV/r)^{\frac{1}{2}} \qquad (3\text{–}10)$$

Making use of eq. (3–5) and using the definition of A from eq. (3–2) we obtain

$$A = exp\, 2(aNcr_1V)^{\frac{1}{2}}[(V/V_p)^{\frac{1}{2}} - 1] \qquad (3\text{–}11)$$

which defines the gas amplification A in terms of experimentally measurable quantities, the voltages, wire radius, etc. A fuller discussion is given in the original paper [R3] and many of the concepts used are described in detail in texts on gas discharges.[L1, D1]

2. Comparison of Theory with Experiment. It will be seen that eq. (3–11) predicts that the gas amplification A should depend on the wire radius (r_1), the capacitance (C) of the counter system, the voltage (V), the pressure of the gas (N), and the kind of gas (a). A series of experiments [R3] was performed to verify the dependence on each of these quantities. The amplification factor was measured, by observing the pulse size in accordance with eq. (3–1), as a function of the voltage, for a counter in which the pressure was varied. Straight lines on semi-logarithmic plots were obtained, the slopes and intercepts being those predicted by eq. (3–11). A typical curve, showing dependence of A on V for various gases, is shown in Fig. 3–1. Next methane-argon mixtures were tested, the total pressure being kept constant but the percentage of each gas being changed. This effectively tested the dependence on a, since a for methane and argon are different (cf. Table 3–1). Again, agreement with the prediction of eq. (3–11) was obtained. Finally various polyatomic gas mixtures were tried and again agreement was obtained. The dependence on wire diameter was also checked, and was found to be correctly predicted by eq. (3–11). The amplification increases as the wire diameter is decreased. The practical limit for wire diameters is approximately 3 mils for counters which are to be normally handled in the laboratory. While counters using 1 mil wire have a higher ampli-

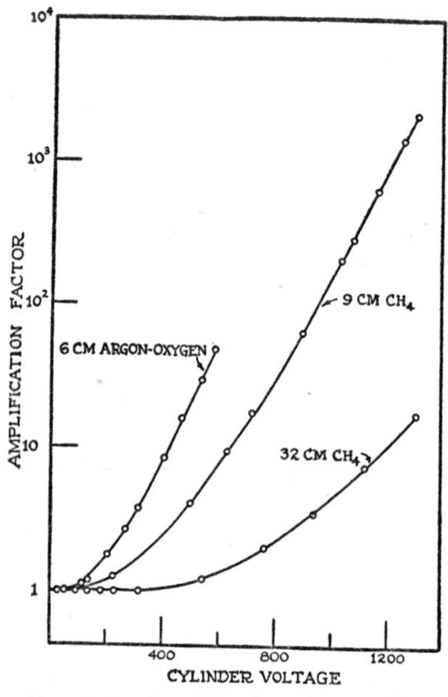

FIG. 3–1. Amplification factor (logarithmic scale) against cylinder voltage for 6-cm argon-oxygen (0.94 A + 0.06 O_2) and two pressures of CH_4. (Rose & Ramsey, *Phys. Rev.* **61**, 199 (1942))

fication factor, this wire is so fragile that the counter may easily be broken in normal use. With the exception of some interesting departures from agreement which we shall discuss below, the good agreement between theory and experiment suggests that the picture we have built up of the avalanche mechanism will satisfactorily describe the proportional counter discharge.

Departures from agreement with the predictions of eq. (3–11) were found in certain cases. These departures are especially interesting in that they throw further light on the nature of the discharge mechanism.

First consider the effects at high voltages. As the voltage is progressively increased, good agreement is maintained until the value of A reaches approximately 10^4. At higher voltages, the pulse size increases with voltage faster than is predicted by eq. (3–11). This is found to occur as the counter enters the region of limited proportionality, traverses this region and goes into the Geiger region. The significance of an increase faster than that predicted by the equation is that something besides the Townsend avalanche is involved. In other words, our limiting simplifying assumptions are not being met. Let us suppose, for example, that ultraviolet photons are formed in the avalanche and reach the cylinder. Here they may liberate photoelectrons which will in turn travel to the wire and start new avalanches. The pulse size will therefore be larger than eq. (3–11), which assumes no photons, predicts. Again, if new electrons are liberated by positive ions reaching the cylinder, the same result occurs. Thus the departure at high voltages is in a direction which indicates that some mechanism, in addition to the simple Townsend avalanche, is operative.

It seems probable that, at amplifications above 10^4, space charge limitations also begin to make themselves felt. The theory of the limitation of the discharge by space charge was developed by the Montgomerys,[M3] and will be discussed fully in the section on Geiger counters. Indeed the main feature of the region of limited proportionality is that large pulses do not increase with voltage as fast as do small pulses. This feature may be ascribed to the effects of space charge, for a large pulse will result in the production of more positive ions and hence more space charge than will a small one. As the field near the wire is reduced by this space charge, the avalanche size will also tend to be decreased, and hence this effect will operate more efficiently on the larger pulses.

Another important departure occurs when gas mixtures are used and the mixture is varied in the direction of an increasing percentage of monatomic gas. Here again another mechanism is evidently at work in addition to the Townsend avalanche, tending to produce more electrons, and hence larger pulses than the avalanche alone, and eq. (3–11) would predict. The experiments reveal an important limitation on eq. (3–11), namely that with monatomic and diatomic gases this equation begins to break down at amplifications of around 100, whereas polyatomic gases may give values of A up to 10,000 before eq. (3–11) ceases adequately to describe the phenomenon. We may tie in this observation by saying that the phenomenon is due to positive ion bombardment of the cylinder. Bombardment by monatomic and diatomic positive ions causes electron emission while polyatomic positive ions, as we shall show, do not. Hence the pure monatomic and diatomic gases, and the mixtures of monatomic with polyatomic, such as equal parts of argon and methane, will exhibit the faster rise of A with V than eq. (3–11) calls for. This positive ion bombardment of the cathode resulting in release of electrons is presumably the main factor in the rapid rise of A with V for low values of A, but this effect is suppressed by the heavier molecules. Thus by adding methane to an argon-filled counter, it is necessary to arrive at a mixture 75% methane and 25% argon before suppression is complete while addition of but 10% of a still larger molecule such as ether to an argon-filled counter produces good agreement with eq. (3–11).

The practical consequence of this circumstance is that any gas or mixture whatever can be made to operate in a proportional counter. However, monatomic and diatomic gas-filled counters are characterized by a much more rapid variation of A with V than are those with polyatomic fillings. The sharp dependence of A on V requires much more critical stabilization and control of the counter operating voltage, and consequently it is usually more convenient to use polyatomic gases in proportional counters. The disadvantage of the polyatomic filling over the monatomic gas lies in (a) the fact that the polyatomic molecules are broken up and consequently the counter changes its characteristics with use, and (b) that the starting and operating potentials of the polyatomic gas counters are generally higher than those filled with monatomic gases. As Spatz has shown [81] a lifetime of about 10^{10} counts may be expected before a polyatomic gas-filled Geiger counter becomes useless due to breakdown of the constituents, and a somewhat longer life may be expected for a proportional counter due to the smaller avalanche size and hence the smaller number of molecules decomposed at each discharge. The starting potentials of counters filled with pure polyatomic gases can be reduced somewhat by adding a monatomic gas; thus, for example, a counter filled with pure methane will actually have its operating potential lowered by adding 10% of argon (the methane content remaining fixed) while the efficiency is also improved by this procedure and its other operating characteristics do not suffer.

In addition to the effects due to positive ions, we must also consider effects due to photons formed in the discharge. Derivation of eq. (3–11) presupposes absence of photons and departures of experimental behavior from agreement with this equation may also indicate that this assumption is, in certain cases, not valid. Photons would produce additional ionization, and consequently the increase of the avalanche size A with V would be more rapid than eq. (3–11) predicts. In the avalanche, photons are presumably formed since collisions result in excitation and atoms in excited states will mostly lose their energy by radiation, the lifetime of these states being of the order of 10^{-8} sec while the mean free time between collisions is somewhat in excess of this figure. Recombination radiation may also occur. As we have pointed out above, recombination is not likely in the avalanche itself, because of the low pressures and high fields. Nevertheless, recombination at the cathode occurs when the positive ions reach it and become neutralized. Again we must consider what happens to the photons.

It should also be pointed out that photons arising from excited atoms of any of the monatomic or diatomic gases normally used in counters, have energies which are mostly greater than the photoelectric threshold of the cathode. Thus, for example, in hydrogen, the Lyman series starts at about 10 volts, and radiation from a helium atom returning to the ground state from, say, the $2P$ level, corresponds in energy to about 20 volts. The photoelectric thresholds of copper and brass are in the neighborhood of 3 volts and consequently the photons from the excited atoms, if they reach the cathode, may be expected to cause emission of photoelectrons. Similarly, the photons which are emitted at the cathode as recombination radiation, also are almost all considerably above the photoelectric threshold in energy. The fact that eq. (3–11), which assumes no photons, fits as well as it does, means that we must explain the absence of both excitation and recombination photons.

The case of recombination photons is discussed at length in the section on self-quenching counters. There it is pointed out that polyatomic ions predissociate instead of radiate upon neutralization. As a result, there are no photons representing recombination radiation in the case of polyatomic molecules. With monatomic and diatomic molecules, such photons will be present and the expected deviations from eq. (3–11), in the direction of faster variation of A with V, occur.

The photons formed by excitation, in the case of monatomic and diatomic gases, are presumably also present, and help to cause the deviations from eq. (3–11) which we have mentioned. There are experimental proofs that photons are present in the discharge. One of these is the experiment on the "localization of the discharge" performed by Wilkening and Kanne [W2] and others. The experiment on localization will be discussed more fully in the next section. There is also an experiment with perforated cathodes, performed by Rose and Korff.[R3] In the latter experiment, A was measured as a function of V for counters with perforated and solid cathodes. It was found that a difference could be detected at large pulse sizes when the counter was filled with a monatomic or diatomic gas. The difference was in the direction of smaller pulses for the perforated cathode, suggesting that the fact that some photons escaped through the perforations made a difference in the pulse size. No difference was observed when the counter was filled with a gas with polyatomic molecules, thus lending further support to the validity of the basic assumption of eq. (3–11) of no photons. The fact that photons are of importance only at large pulse sizes is presumably due to the low photoelectric efficiency. Only a few photons will be generated in a small avalanche, and only a small fraction (10^{-4} or so for most commonly used cathodes) of these will add electrons to the avalanche. Consequently the amplification A must approach the order of 10^4 before excitation photons begin to contribute appreciably to the avalanche size.

The behavior of proportional counters at low values of A has been studied by Rose and Ramsey.[R4] They have investigated the portion of the amplification factor vs. voltage curve near the threshold for proportional counter action, both above and below the threshold. As might be expected from consideration of the statistical nature of the avalanche process, the threshold is not an abrupt phenomenon, but the observed curves gradually trend toward the horizontal. The threshold voltage predicted by eq. (3–11) is the voltage corresponding to the point where the straight line portion of the curve, if extrapolated downward (see Fig. 3–1), would intersect the abscissa for unit A. Fig. 3–2 shows the curves obtained at higher values of A. The experimental curve departs from the computed curve because the theory neglects fluctuations and assumes average energies for the electrons in the avalanche.

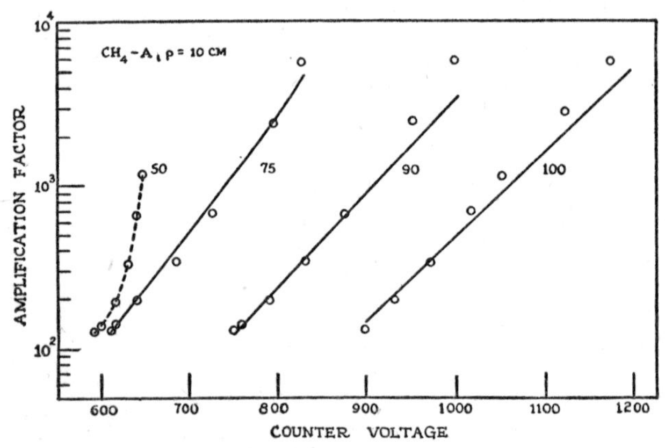

FIG. 3–2. The amplification factor (logarithmic scale) plotted against counter voltage for various relative concentrations in CH_4-A mixtures at 10-cm pressure. The points are experimental and the full curves are theoretical with one point adjusted (see equation (3–11)). The numbers affixed to the curves give the relative concentration of CH_4 in percent. The dimensions of the counter were: wire diameter 0.075 mm; Cu. cylinder, diameter 1 cm and length 3 cm. (From M. E. Rose and S. A. Korff, *Phys. Rev.* 59, 850–859 (1941))

Such fluctuations are percentagewise largest for values of A just greater than unity, and become unimportant at values of A greater than 10 or 20.

C. Counters for Special Purposes

1. Neutron Counters. *a. Counters for Slow Neutrons.* To detect slow neutrons, proportional counters filled with boron trifluoride (BF_3), which is a gas at normal room temperature, may be used.[K3] A neutron entering this gas may interact with the boron nucleus according to the reaction:

$$_0n^1 + {}_5B^{10} \rightarrow {}_5B^{11}{}^* \rightarrow {}_3Li^7 + {}_2He^4 \qquad (3\text{–}12)$$

This reaction has a large cross section (a high probability of occurrence). The resulting alpha particle, and also the recoiling lithium nucleus, produce dense ionization along a short range or path. The proportional counter can therefore distinguish between pulses produced by this reaction and the smaller pulses produced by beta rays.

The reaction eq. (3–12) results in the liberation of about 2.5 Mev, which appears as kinetic energy of the resulting lithium and helium fragments. Parenthetically it may be added that this is an observed figure and is about 0.4 Mev less than the value computed from the masses, the difference being ascribed to the lithium nucleus which is believed to emerge in an excited state. By applying the principle of the conservation of momentum, it may be readily calculated that the alpha particle carries about 1.6 Mev and the recoiling lithium nucleus about 0.9. The two particles travel in opposite directions. This phenomenon is of importance if the disintegration takes place near the wall of the counter, since one particle may strike the counter cathode but the other will go out into the gas.

An evolution of 2.5 Mev in ionization means, at roughly 30 ev per ion, the production of some 83,000 ion-pairs. Applying eq. (3–1), we find if A is taken as unity and C as 10 micromicrofarads, V will be 1.33×10^{-3} volts. If A is made about 100, then V will be sufficiently large to operate many electronic circuits directly (see Chapter 7) and to display on an oscilloscope screen. Values of A between 100 and 10^4 can readily be obtained by choosing suitable counter voltages, and a BF_3 counter will still be operating in the proportional region.

Commercial boron trifluoride is composed of a mixture of the isotopes B^{10} and B^{11}, roughly 20% of the former and 80% of the latter. Unfortunately reaction eq. (3–12) will only work for the B^{10} isotope and the B^{11} component performs no useful function. When the techniques of isotope separation are developed to the point that boron trifluoride consisting almost entirely of B^{10} can be prepared, an increase in detection sensitivity of a factor of five will be possible. The measured [B2] cross section for process eq. (3–12), when the isotope ratio is taken into account, comes out to be $\sigma = 550 \times 10^{-24}$ sq cm, for "thermal" neutrons in equilibrium in water, a figure which we will adopt for all subsequent discussion.

Process eq. (3–12) operates for slow neutrons. The figure cited refers to "thermal" neutrons, i.e., neutrons in thermal equilibrium in paraffin or water at room temperature. For faster neutrons, the cross section is known to vary inversely as the velocity. We may therefore write

$$\sigma(v) = \sigma/v \qquad (3\text{–}13)$$

where σ is the cross section for the process under discussion.

The efficiency of a neutron counter we shall define as the probability that a neutron, if passing through the counter, will be captured and hence detected. The probability of capture, and of process eq. (3–12) occurring, is evidently the cross section eq. (3–13) per atom times the average path length for the neutrons passing through the sensitive volume of the counter, times the number of B^{10} nuclei per cc in the sensitive volume. The counting rate, or number of captures per sec, depends on the flux of neutrons and the probability of capture. Consider a counter exposed to a flux of neutrons of various velocities. The number of counts per second n will be given by

$$n = ULp \int i(v)\sigma(v)\,dv \qquad (3\text{–}14)$$

U is the sensitive volume of the counter, L the Loschmidt number and p the pressure in atmospheres, $i(v)\,dv$ the flux of neutrons crossing a sq cm area per second with velocity between v and $v + dv$, and $\sigma(v)$ the cross section for capture. But

$$i(v) = \rho v \qquad (3\text{–}15)$$

where ρ is the density or number of neutrons per cc of all velocities and v is the velocity. Substituting eqs. (3–15) and

(3–13) in eq. (3–14), the velocity drops out, we may integrate at once and we obtain

$$n = ULp\rho\sigma_B v_B \qquad (3\text{–}16)$$

Here σ_B is the capture cross section for some known velocity v_B. Numerically we may take these as the thermal cross section cited above and thermal velocity. It is to be noted that the counter measures the density of neutrons ρ, regardless of velocity per cc, and not the flux, or number i of neutrons crossing a sq cm area per second. The flux cannot be determined unless the velocity is known. This property of measuring the density is a ccmmon characteristic of all detectors obeying the $1/v$ law (eq. (3–13)), and is well known in nuclear physics experiments.

If we consider neutrons which all have (nearly) the same velocity, e.g., which are all thermal, then we can compute the efficiency of such a counter. The efficiency E, defined as the fraction of a flux of neutrons which produces counts, is evidently given by the ratio of the counting rate (e.g., eq. (3–16) per unit volume) to the flux, and hence by the relation

$$E = Lp\sigma_B d, \qquad (3\text{–}17)$$

where d is the average path through the counter of the neutrons to be measured, and where σ_B is the capture cross section for neutrons of the particular velocity being measured. The calculation of the average path through a cylinder presents certain analytical difficulty in the general case, although certain special cases have been computed by Swann.[S2] To a sufficient degree of approximation we may take d as a diameter. For example, considering counting slow neutrons with a 7-cm diameter counter with one atmosphere BF_3, $p = 1$, $d = 7$, $N = 2.7 \times 10^{19}$, $\sigma = 550 \times 10^{-24}$, E will be about 10.4%. A smaller counter with $p = 0.1$ atm, $d = 2$ cm would have an efficiency of 0.29% for thermal neutrons. A counter is not made more efficient by making it longer, although the total counts recorded will increase.

It is also evident that the efficiency depends on the neutron velocities, the above examples assuming the value of σ appropriate for a flux of thermal neutrons. For higher average energies, σ must be decreased according to the $1/v$ law, i.e., must be multiplied by v_t/v_m, where v_m is the velocity of the neutrons measured and v_t the thermal velocity. Thus the efficiency will depend on the arrangement of scattering and "slowing down" material around the counter.

In computing the number of neutrons to be expected at a given distance from a source, it must be recalled that because of scattering the inverse square law does not apply, and that the processes of the diffusion theory must be used. Since almost any source produces neutrons with relatively high energies and since almost any substance slows them down, it is evident that the energy distribution will be a function of the distance from the source and the geometrical arrangement of the counter, source and surrounding material, as well as of the nature of the source and the type of matter nearby. The procedures for computing the result for any given arrangement are well known in the diffusion theory and are outside of the scope of this treatment.

It is possible to measure the number of neutrons in a given energy range with BF_3 counters by making measurements with and without certain types of absorbing screens. Thus, for example, a cadmium shield of ½ to 1 mm thickness will be practically opaque to thermal neutrons and practically transparent to neutrons of more than one volt energy. Similarly, borax or boron carbide shields of various thicknesses may be used. In these, the absorption will occur inversely as the neutron velocity, and consequently the effect of any given thickness may be computed. In these calculations, account must be taken of the contribution to the slowing down process due to the water of crystallization in the borax.

It follows from eq. (3–17) that greater efficiency is secured at high pressures of BF_3. The practical limit of BF_3 pressures is determined (a) by the fact that high pressures require high operating potentials, and (b) by the fact that the pulses due to beta rays increase in size with increasing pressure. Since beta rays have ranges which are long compared to the dimensions of the chamber, at high pressures, more of the range is included. The disintegration particles are entirely stopped in the gas at moderate pressures and therefore increasing pressure produces no increase in neutron pulse size. Thus the ratio of neutron-to-beta background varies with the pressure and the practical limit is reached when the beta pulses become nearly as large as the neutron pulses.

As an alternative to filling the counter with some gas in which disintegrations are produced as discussed above, counters are sometimes filled with an inert gas and lined with a solid substance from which the disintegration particles emerge. Such a particle must get out into the volume of the counter in order to be detected. The maximum efficiency of a counter of this type lined with boron for slow neutrons will be given by the relation

$$E_{\max} = (N\rho/\mu)R_B\sigma_B \tag{3-18}$$

where N is Avogadro's number, ρ is the density of the material of the wall, μ is its atomic weight, R_B is the range of the alpha particles in boron and σ_B the capture cross section of the wall material (usually boron) for neutrons at the velocity measured. For a boron-lined counter and for thermal neutrons, $E_{\max}$ is about 5%. The boron lining need be only 0.1 mm thick, and added thickness will merely reduce the efficiency. The same considerations would apply to a counter lined with uranium and operating by fission, except that alpha particles originating in the uranium would have to be taken into account by setting the minimum detectable pulse size at a high value. Any gas may of course be used in such a counter.

Finally it should be pointed out that other gases in which neutrons may produce disintegrations have a possible usefulness in such counters. A uranium compound gas may be used since the fission fragments have a high specific ionization and would produce large pulses.

b. Counters for fast neutrons. Proportional counters can also be used to detect fast neutrons.[K4] In this case, it is customary to make use of "recoils." A fast neutron may collide with a nucleus of one of the atoms in the gas of the counter or in the surrounding material and cause that nucleus to recoil through the counter. Such recoiling nuclei usually have a high specific ionization and produce counts. The total number of recoil counts n_r per sec produced in the gas of the counter will be given by

$$n_r = UNp \int_{v_{\min}}^{v_{\max}} I(v)\sigma_r(v)\, dv \tag{3–19}$$

where $I(v)\, dv$ is the flux of neutrons per sq cm per second in the velocity interval dv and the recoil cross section σ_r is taken as varying with energy. The experimental evaluation of the limits of integration is discussed below. It will be observed that this is an integral equation and that a simple solution will occur when the cross section may be taken as a constant over the energy range discussed. For example, for hydrogen, the neutron-proton scattering cross section is known to vary between 0.5 and 1.5×10^{-24} in the energy range between 400 kev and 4 Mev. A rough order-of-magnitude estimate of the neutron flux may be obtained, therefore, by taking the cross section as a constant equal to 1×10^{-24} sq cm.

The efficiency of a recoil counter is defined as the fraction of fast neutrons passing through the counter which produces recoils, it being assumed that virtually every recoil produces a count. The efficiency may be computed for any particular velocity by applying eq. (3–17) and writing the recoil cross section σ_r instead of σ_B. Since the recoil cross section is small, the efficiency of this counter is low. For example, a counter 2 cm in diameter and filled to 28 cm pressure with hydrogen will have an efficiency of about 10^{-5}. The values of the recoil cross section have been measured by various observers for different substances and generally are of the order of 10^{-24} sq cm.

For complex molecules, eq. (3–19) must be modified to take account of the cross section of each atom of which the molecule is composed. For example, in the case of BF_3 it would include a term $(\sigma_B + 3\sigma_F)$.

Let us now consider the meaning of the limits of integration in eq. (3–19). The lower limit signifies that the recoiling nucleus shall have enough energy to produce a count. In terms of eq. (3–19), the velocity v of the recoiling nucleus shall be greater than $v_{\min}$. It follows from elementary "billiard ball" mechanics that a neutron of energy E and unit mass colliding with a nucleus (other than a proton) of mass M will produce a recoil with an average energy about $2E/M$ and a maximum energy of $4E/M$. For protons the maximum energy transfer is E and the average $E/2$. Consequently a counter so adjusted as not to detect any pulse liberating less than 50 kev as ionization in the counter will, if filled with hydrogen, detect neutrons with average energies in excess of 100 kev, but if filled with argon will on the average not detect neutrons with energies below 1 Mev.

Recoiling atoms will also be ejected from the walls of the cylinder. The number of counts due to wall records, M_w, will be given by

$$n_w = \frac{N\rho F}{2\mu} \int_{v_{\min}}^{v_{\max}} \sigma_r(v) R(v) i(v)\, dv \qquad (3\text{–}20)$$

where N is Avogadro's number, ρ the density of the material of the wall, μ its atomic weight, σ_r the recoil cross section of the nuclei of this substance for the neutrons to be measured, $i(v)$ the flux of neutrons per cm^2 per sec, per unit velocity interval, F the cross-sectional area of the counter exposed to the flux, and R the range in cm of the recoiling nuclei in the material of the wall. The factor ½ arises from an integration to give the average number of recoils actually emerging, assuming a random distribution in angle of the recoils. If from this expression for the total recoils entering the gas from the walls, be subtracted those which have insufficient energy after emergence to produce a count, it will be seen that wall recoils are only important compared to recoils in the gas if (a) the material of the walls is light, (b) the neutrons are of high energy, and (c) the gas pressure in the counter is small, and hence the recoils produced in the gas are few.

The upper limit of integration becomes of importance only in the case of hydrogen. If the recoiling proton has a very high energy, it may pass through the counter without losing enough energy in ionization to produce a recorded count. The upper and lower energy limits are established by the dimensions of the counter, the nature of the gas in the counter, and the energy spectrum of the incident neutrons, as well as by the voltage at which the counter is operated. For a heavy gas such as argon, the neutron energy necessary to produce a recoil too energetic to be counted is so large as to be beyond the range normally encountered and the limit may be considered as infinity. It is evident that increasing the voltage on the counter, other things being equal, is the equivalent of decreasing the lower limit of integration. The upper limit is also raised, in those cases where it is not already effectively infinite.

A proportional counter, whether counting disintegrations or recoils, will also count any other event in which a large amount of ionization is produced. Among such events will be giant showers, nuclear disintegrations produced by the cosmic radiation, and alpha particles present as natural contamination in the walls of the counter. The number of counts due to these several causes may be regarded as a background if surrounding conditions are not changed and can be determined by obvious procedures and subtracted from the counting rate. An important problem in the use of BF_3 counters lies in separating the disintegrations from the recoils. This may be done by varying the integration limits and by the use of cadmium and boron

ORDER
MENT
Laboratory

PURCHASE ORDER
No. A

shields as discussed earlier. Further, the number of recoils may be independently measured by using a counter filled with some gas other than BF_3, which does not suffer disintegrations.

2. Counters for Heavy Ionizing Particles. Proportional counters are well adapted to detecting alpha particles and protons, and indeed alpha particles were the first entities to be counted in the early uses of counters. An alpha particle has a high specific ionization, and produces on the average some 30,000 ion-pairs per cm in air at STP. Indeed it produces nearly twice this number near the end of its range. The average electron or cosmic ray particle may produce 30 to 100 ion-pairs per cm, and even a slow electron near the end of its range will not produce one tenth as many ions per cm as an alpha particle. Therefore a proportional counter, which produces a pulse whose magnitude is proportional to the number of ions initially formed, will distinguish between alpha particles and electrons with no difficulty at all.

The range of a 1 Mev proton in air is about 2.3 cm. Hence it produces about 12,000 ion-pairs per cm or just over a third as much ionization as does an alpha particle. A proton of this energy is consequently also easy to detect and to distinguish from beta particles.

In detecting alpha particles or protons, any gas whatever may be used in the counter. Some gases are more desirable than others, but any gas can be made to work. Thus, for example, air or oxygen should be avoided because of the possible complications resulting from the formation of negative ions. Particles have a high specific ionization in argon, and this gas also has a low threshold voltage. However, in common with other monatomic gases, argon exhibits a rapid variation of pulse size (amplification) with voltage at high amplification, and hence is somewhat less easy to work with than are the polyatomic gases, which, while they have higher thresholds generally, require less critical stabilization of operating potentials.

One problem in connection with alpha particle and proton counters is to get the particle to be detected into the counter. This is often accomplished by projecting the particle in through a thin foil. The details of possible construction of counters of this type are discussed in the chapter on construction. In other studies, the counter may be directly sealed onto the experimental system in which the particles are accelerated. In this case, the type of gas in the counter is usually determined by the gases used in the rest of the system. Again, weak sources may be put directly into the counter, and some gas flowed through at atmospheric pressure. Illustrations are given in Chapter 5.

The pulse size obtained on the wire of a proportional counter is given by eq. (3–1). The number of ions formed in the initial ionizing event is in turn determined by the specific ionization of the particle being studied in the gas with which the counter is filled. Hence the pulse size V will be given by

$$V = Asple/c \tag{3–21}$$

where s is the specific ionization, in ions per cm per atm produced by the particle in the gas in question, p is the pressure in atmospheres and l is the length of the path of the particle through the sensitive portion of the counter. The specific ionization s averaged over the entire path can be obtained from the range of a particle. Thus, for example, the range of 2 Mev alpha particles is about 1.05 cm in air at 15° C and 760 mm pressure.[B2] Since each ion-pair produced in air requires the expenditure of some 30 ev, the specific ionization s will be about 6×10^4 ions per cm. The values of s for cosmic ray particles (fast mesotrons at sea level) are found in Chapter 4, Table 1. The large pulses formed by particles having high specific ionization may, for example, be displayed on an oscilloscope screen, and recording circuits (see Chapter 7) may be made to discriminate against the smaller pulses such as a beta or gamma ray background and record only the large ones.

CHAPTER 4

THE GEIGER COUNTERS

A. Non-selfquenching Counters

1. Theory. *a. Empirical Description of the Discharge Mechanism.* In this section we shall discuss the operation of the counter containing any monatomic or diatomic gas or mixtures thereof. As will be explained, such gases and mixtures pro-

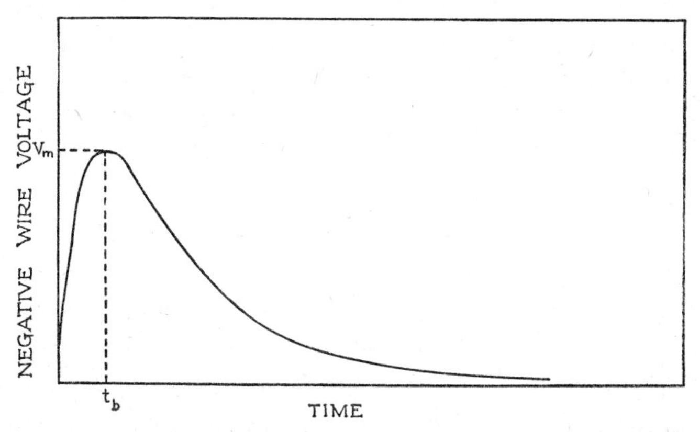

Fig. 4–1. A typical voltage pulse from a selfquenching counter. As viewed on an oscilloscope with a linear sweep, the voltage across R during a pulse is shown here. (After H. G. Stever, *Phys. Rev.* **61**, 39 (1942))

duce non-selfquenching counters. We shall discuss operation at voltages above the threshold for Geiger counting action. In this voltage region all pulses produced by the counter are of the same size, and in general, they are a volt or more in amplitude.

The pulse produced by a counter, if viewed on an oscilloscope screen, has a shape roughly represented in Fig. 4–1. It will be noted that the pulse is characterized by a rapid growth to full value, and then by a slower recovery to normal. The first part is called the "break" as the counter breaks down into a discharge, and the break takes place in a time of the order of a microsecond. The break is due to the sudden onset of ionization inside the counter and to the collection of charge on the central wire, thereby altering its potential. The return of the wire potential to normal is a function of the time constant of the fundamental circuit, Fig. 1–1. It is evident that if the wire is suddenly given a potential V_0 by collecting ions, then its potential V at a time t seconds later will be given by

$$V = V_0 e^{-t/RC} \tag{4–1}$$

where R and C are the resistance and capacity of the circuit. The total charge Q collected on the wire per pulse is given by

$$Q = \int I dt \tag{4–2}$$

where I is the current flowing and t the time. For small pulses, the measured values of Q are of the order of magnitude of 10^{-10} to 10^{-12} coulomb, corresponding to a current of 10^{-6} ampere flowing for 10^{-5} sec or so. The measurement of Q we will discuss later in detail. This charge arriving on a capacity of 10^{-11} farads produces a pulse of about one volt in amplitude, and, following eq. (1–1), indicates the collection of about 6.2×10^7 electrons. This represents a small pulse at the lower end of the Geiger region, larger pulses being up to 100 times this size.

The early experimenters employed a high resistance for the purpose of "quenching" the discharge. Such counters were therefore called resistance-quenched counters. An empirical description of the operation of the resistance may be obtained by considering the corona mechanism. A continuous discharge is sometimes called a "corona" and we shall consider this, following the treatment developed by Werner [W1] and others. The fundamental circuit of a counter with resistance quenching is that shown in Fig. 1–1. If a voltmeter and ammeter be connected in the battery circuit, it is found that a steady discharge cannot be maintained inside the counter, unless the voltage exceeds a certain minimum value. A continuous discharge also requires that the current in the gas shall exceed a certain minimum value. The corona characteristic of this counter is shown in Fig. 4–2. The minimum voltage and current, labeled V_{min} and i_{min} are shown in Fig. 4–2.

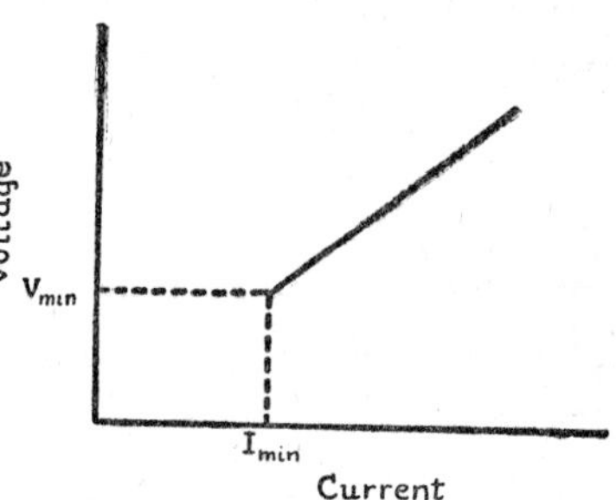

FIG. 4–2. Corona characteristic of a counter.

Any current flowing in the counter must also flow through the resistance R, which has been called the quenching resistance. When the counter is operating at a voltage V_o, larger than V_{min}, then the overvoltage on the counter is equal to $V_o - V_{\text{min}}$. When the count takes place, the current flows, and a voltage drop Ri_{min} is, in effect, removed from the operating potential. If $V_{\text{min}} > V_o - Ri_{\text{min}}$, the operating potential drops below V_{min}, and since this voltage is no longer sufficient to sustain the corona, the discharge in the counter ceases and the counter is said to be quenched. If the voltage V_o is raised, a potential will be reached at which the overvoltage exceeds the product Ri_{min} by an appreciable amount, and the counter will then tend to go into a continuous discharge. The plateau or operating range of such a counter should therefore be Ri_{min} volts in extent. On this view the discharge is terminated because of the resistance. We must, however, accept this interpretation with reservations.

The pulse size produced by a counter is defined as the change in potential of the wire. On the basis of the above mechanism, this is evidently equal to the overvoltage. The picture which we may obtain in this way is not strictly accurate and the departures will be discussed below. Indeed, as the Montgomerys [M3] and Danforth [D2] have pointed out, the pulse may be considerably larger than the overvoltage. The counter in this case is said to "overshoot" and the potential of the wire drops below the Geiger threshold. The phenomenon of overshooting will be discussed below.

Unfortunately resistance quenching places severe limitations on the use of such a counter. The minimum currents have been measured for various counters and are of the order of one-tenth of a microampere to 2 or 3 microamperes. Suppose we consider a counter with a minimum current of 0.1 microampere. If operated with resistance R of 10^8 ohms, the product Ri_{min} would be about 10 volts. This would constitute a range in which it would be possible for the resistance-quenching mechanism to work. A "plateau" of 10 volts is quite small, and makes the operation of such a counter difficult and unstable. It is therefore necessary to employ larger resistances. A resistance of the order of 10^9 ohms or more was customarily used in the earlier work. Increasing the resistance still further would increase the usable width of the plateau. Similarly, anything that could be done to increase the minimum current in the counter would also increase the usable plateau. As Werner [W3] and others have emphasized, a high minimum current is desirable.

However, increasing the size of the quenching resistance introduces a serious limitation, since the recovery time of the counter in the fundamental circuit in Fig. 1–1 is determined by the exponential time constant RC, eq. (4–1). The capacity of the counter wire and attached electronic circuits can hardly be reduced below a few centimeters, and if we take the capacity as 10^{-11} farad and a resistance as 10^9 ohms as indicated above, then the time constant RC is of the order of 0.01 sec. This time constant limits the rapidity with which the counter will count. In any random distribution of the counting events, there is a considerable probability that two counts will arrive within a short time of one another. The counter just mentioned would be losing an appreciable fraction of its counts if it had a recovery time constant of 0.01 sec and were counting at the rate of ten random counts per sec. Indeed, no satisfactory compromise is possible between the recovery time constant and the length of plateau necessary for stability, which both increase as R. It is for this reason that the use of resistance quenching has been virtually abandoned, and vacuum-tube circuits which accomplish the same result much faster are used instead. Several such vacuum tube circuits are described in detail in Chapter 7. These circuits drop the operating potential of the counter below $V_{\min}$ for a period of 10^{-4} sec or so, allowing the discharge to cease and then return the potential to normal.

b. Discussion of the atomic mechanism. When the quenching mechanism was further examined by Montgomery and Montgomery,[M3] the following picture was arrived at. Let us suppose that an ionizing event occurs and an electron is formed somewhere within the volume of the counter. This electron is drawn by the field toward the central wire and in the neighborhood of the central wire produces additional electrons by the Townsend avalanche process. The avalanche is over in a very short time, owing to the high mobility of electrons. The electrons are actually collected on the wire in a fraction of a microsecond. As Ramsey's [R5] experiments have shown, during this time the positive ions left behind by this avalanche mechanism have virtually not moved at all. The wire is therefore surrounded by a positive ion sheath and this positive ion sheath now begins to travel outwards. The sheath crosses the counter, eventually arrives at the cylinder and is there neutralized.

Immediately after the electron avalanche has taken place and the positive ion sheath has been formed, the field conditions in the neighborhood of the wire are fundamentally and radically altered. Between the sheath and the wire the field is much reduced. It may be reduced to such a value that no further Townsend avalanches can occur. The discharge then ceases. It is thus the positive ion sheath which actually quenches the discharge. As the Montgomerys [M3] have pointed out, the discharge is quenched in spite of the quenching resistance which actually permits charge to leak back onto the wire, and if made too low, would tend to counteract the effect of the positive space charge by allowing the wire potential to recover rapidly. A better name would be the "recovery resistance," as this expresses its true function.

The discharge, having thus been quenched by the positive ion sheath, will now remain quenched as long as no further electrons are formed by any subsequent process. The positive ion sheath travels outward to the cylinder. When it reaches the cylinder, secondary electrons may be created by positive ion bombardment. The details of this process are quite complex and we shall adopt a simplified view. We shall assume that a positive ion, approaching the surface of the metal, draws an electron out through the potential barrier at the surface. This electron then neutralizes the positive ion. The positive ion as it returns to its ground-state will emit its characteristic recombination radiation in one or more spectral lines. For ions such as argon, the recombination spectrum lies in the ultraviolet in a spectral region, the quantum energies of which are larger than the work function of the material of the cylinder. Many of the recombination quanta thus emitted will reach the cylinder and one must therefore consider the emission of photoelectrons. The photoelectric efficiency and the work function of the various surfaces are known and one can therefore estimate the number of secondary electrons which are likely to be emitted when recombination radiation of a given wavelength strikes the metal. The photoelectric threshold of copper lies at about 3000 Ångstroms (roughly 4 volts), and the photoelectric efficiency of many of the surfaces used in counters is of the order of magnitude of 10^{-4}, although this figure can be altered an order of magnitude in either direction by suitable choice of surfaces. Thus, if 10^4 photons strike the cylinder, it is probable that one secondary electron will be formed and the avalanche process will therefore repeat.

The meaning of V_{min} now becomes clear. V_{min} is that voltage at which at least one secondary electron is produced by every sheath of positive ions as it goes out to the cylinder and is there neutralized. If every sheath moving out produces at least one secondary electron, this secondary electron starts a new avalanche which produces a new sheath, and the discharge will continue indefinitely. This continuous discharge is not, as we have pointed out before, really continuous in time, but consists of a series of pulses or spurts at close and somewhat overlapping intervals.

We may now understand the operation of the quenching resistance or the quenching circuit. The function of these is to keep the potential of the wire below V_{min} until all positive ions have been neutralized. Once this has been accomplished, no further mechanism for the ejection of secondary electrons exists and the discharge is therefore terminated. The circuit or resistance may then return the counter to its normal operating potential, and it will then be sensitive to the next event. To reduce the insensitive time, it is desirable that this return to operating conditions should be as quick as possible and may, in general, be of the order of a few times 10^{-4} sec.

In some cases, the initial Townsend avalanche is not large, and the positive ion sheath does not contain enough ions to lower the field in the neighborhood of the wire below the sustaining potential of the discharge. Photons formed in the initial avalanche will travel to the cylinder. When they strike the cylinder, they will cause the ejection of further photoelectrons, and these photoelectrons, coming into the region near the wire, will then cause further avalanches. The result of this phenomenon is the process of "multiple breaks" observed by Ramsey and the Montgomerys.[R5] These experimenters were able to photograph on an oscilloscope the successive changes in the potential of the wire as several groups of electrons due to the photons formed in the various avalanches arrived on the wire. The wire thus attained its full potential drop, not as the result of one electron avalanche, but as the result of several in quick succession. A curve of this phenomenon is shown in Fig. 4–3. When the field near the wire attains a value so low that no further avalanches can be supported, the discharge ceases. The subsequent recovery of the counter to a new operating potential is controlled not by the internal mechanism but by the speed of the external quenching circuit of resistance.

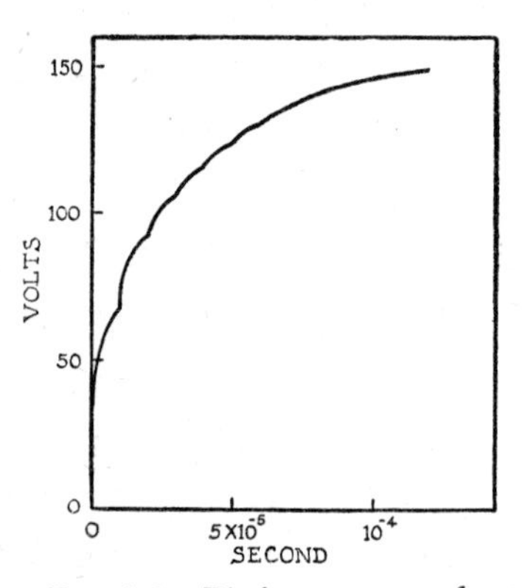

FIG. 4–3. Discharge curve of a counter with a large capacity connected to the counter wire. (C. G. and D. D. Montgomery, *Phys. Rev.* 57, 1035 (1940))

c. Calculation of the efficiency of counters. We will define the efficiency of a counter as the probability that the counter will count when an event of the type to be measured takes place within it. Thus, for example, the efficiency of a beta ray counter counting electrons is equal to the probability that the counter will discharge when one electron is formed inside it or enters it from the outside. Since it is only necessary to have one electron formed inside the counter to start an avalanche, the efficiency of a counter may be readily computed.[D3, C3] We shall consider the probability that any given ionizing event will produce one electron within the active volume of the counter.

Suppose it is desired to detect a particle such as a cosmic ray or a high-speed electron which is passing through the counter. Let x represent the average number of electrons produced by the particle to be detected as it passes through the counter. Then the probability that such a particle can pass through the counter and produce no electrons is e^{-x}. The efficiency G of this counter, which is the probability that one electron shall be produced, is therefore equal to $1 - e^{-x}$.

The evaluation of x is straightforward if the specific ionization of the particle to be detected is known. The specific ionization is defined as the number of ion-pairs per cm of path per atm which is left behind in the gas when the particle in question passes through it. Since high energy rays may produce secondaries capable of producing further ionization, it is customary to distinguish between the total specific ionization and the primary specific ionization. The total specific ionization determines the rate of energy-loss by the primary particle. The primary specific ionization is that used in counter efficiency calculations, since it is the number of ion-pairs formed by the primary, and not the energy of each, that determines whether a counter will register a count. The specific ionization for fast electrons and for cosmic rays has been measured in various gases and is given in Table 4–1 below. Let us consider a few numerical cases. Suppose a counter of about 1 in. diameter is used for the detection of a cosmic ray. Let us further suppose that this counter is filled to a typical pressure of about 0.1 atm of argon. The total number of electrons which would be left behind in the counter by the passage of a cosmic ray mesotron through it would therefore be equal to slp, where s is the specific ionization, l the length of the path through the counter and p the pressure of the gas in atmosphere. Thus, we may write for the efficiency the relation:

$$G = 1 - e^{-slp} \tag{4–3}$$

In case cited, if the average path through this counter for the particles in question were about 2 cm, and the specific ionization for argon were taken as 30 ions per cm per atm from Table 4–1, it is evident that on the average 6 ions would be created in the volume of the counter by the passage of the average mesotron through it. The chance that no ion would be created would be e^{-6} and the efficiency of the counter would therefore be 99.8%. Similarly, if the same counter were filled with hydrogen at the same pressure, since the value s is so much less for hydrogen, there would on the average be 1.2 ions left behind in the counter by the passage of each ray. The efficiency in this case would then be about 70%. From this discussion it will be readily appreciated that it is important to employ a gas using high specific ionization, or with high pressure in order to obtain a counter with appreciable efficiency. A counter will be inefficient if the pressure is too low. Several counters which have been reported in the literature employing gases with pressures of about 2 cm are evidently undesirable on the basis of efficiency.

TABLE 4–1. SPECIFIC IONIZATION, s, IN IONS PER CM PER ATM, PRODUCED BY HIGH SPEED COSMIC-RAY PARTICLES, IN GASES WITH n_e ELECTRONS PER ATOM OR MOLECULE

Gas	n_e	s	Reference
Hydrogen (H_2)	2	6.0 ± 0.2	C3, D3
Helium	2	5.9	C3
Helium	2	6.5	H6
Air	14.4	21	D3
Argon	18	29.4	C3
Methane (CH_4)	10	16	S6
Neon	10	12	S8
$C_2H_5(OH)$	26	33 or 42 *	H6
BF_3	32	44	S. K. †
Xenon	54	44 **	S. K. †

* Calculated: 33 if empirical relation between s and n_e is assumed, viz., $s = 1.1n_e + 3$. The value 42 is obtained if s for $3H_2$, $\frac{1}{2}O_2$ and C_2 are added. The straight line empirical formula breaks down for $n_e = 1$ and 0. It is at best a rough guide to the trend of s.** The value for Xe seems low but possibly the departure from the calculated value 65 is traceable to the tightness of the binding of the innermost electrons and screening.

† Unpublished.

The efficiency of a counter is of extreme importance. It is important not only when such a counter is used to count single particles, as is done in medical experiments, but is also of vital concern in coincidence studies. In coincidence work, the inefficiencies are multiplicative and in many such experiments an efficiency of less than 98% cannot be tolerated if good results are desired. Indeed, efficiencies of less than this should not be employed for any measuring problem, since too many unknown factors may cause measurements with an inefficient counter to be unreproducible. Since it is easy to make highly efficient counters, there is no reason to tolerate inefficient ones, except for certain special problems which we will discuss later.

We may consider the efficiency of a counter in detecting alpha rays. An alpha particle produces a very high specific ionization. It is possible to compute the number of ions per cm from the well known Bragg curve. The probability that an ion should be formed within the volume of the counter is unity if an alpha particle expends any fraction of its range in the gas of the counter. It is therefore only necessary for an alpha particle to traverse or end its range in any portion of the sensitive volume in order for a count to be recorded. Similar arguments may be advanced in the case of electrons nearing the ends of their ranges. The specific ionization for an electron near the end of its range is obtainable from the ionization curve for electrons. The ionization is heaviest toward the end of the range, and therefore every electron of energy of a few hundred volts or so which enters the sensitive volume of the counter will produce a count. The difficulties which may be encountered in measuring beta radiation from weak radioactive sources with an inefficient counter are at once apparent. Such a weak beta ray may just be able to get through the wall of the counter. If the efficiency of the counter is not high, many of these beta rays may come to the ends of their ranges in some portion of the counter which is not sensitive, or may enter the sensitive volume and still not be detected. The possible errors that an inefficient counter may produce are therefore uncertain and difficult to correct.

Counters may also be used for detecting photons and gamma radiation. In designing a counter for this purpose, it is customary to provide two features which would be undesirable in beta ray or cosmic ray counters. These are (a) a window transparent to radiation and (b) a surface on the cylinder with maximum photoelectric efficiency for the particular radiation. The cathode of the counter may in addition be cut, perforated or otherwise so arranged that a large aperture exists through which the photons to be measured reach the photoelectric surface.

The number of photoelectrons formed in the gas of the counter is usually small compared to the number ejected from the walls. In the case of high-energy gamma radiation, a high-energy photon may produce a Compton electron in the gas of the counter or may eject an electron from the wall by one of several processes. In any event, the gamma ray will be detected only if it produces an electron somewhere within the sensitive volume. Since the photoelectric efficiencies of surfaces are, in general, quite low, a counter will ordinarily have a rather poor efficiency in detecting gamma radiation.

We may also discuss the effect on the efficiency of the introduction of heavy organic vapors into counters. Counters employing argon with an addition of alcohol or other organic vapor have been in common use for some time. Usually, the vapor pressure of the organic substance is of the order of 1 or 2 cm. If the pressure of the argon is between 0.1 and 0.2 atm, the majority of the ionization formed within the counter by the primary ionizing event will be in the form of argon ions rather than organic ions. The efficiency calculations can therefore be made on the basis of the argon content of the counter, and the contribution due to the alcohol will be small. The specific ionization of various types of radiation in the organic vapors has, in general, not been measured, but there appears no reason to suppose that this would be different in order of magnitude from the specific ionization in other gases. The specific ionization is roughly proportional to the number of electrons per molecule and so will be fairly high for alcohol. Hazen [H6] estimates that it is probably about 42 ions per cm for ethyl alcohol. The addition of 10% or so of alcohol vapor to an argon-filled counter will therefore slightly improve the efficiency which is already high. Greisen and his collaborators [G5]

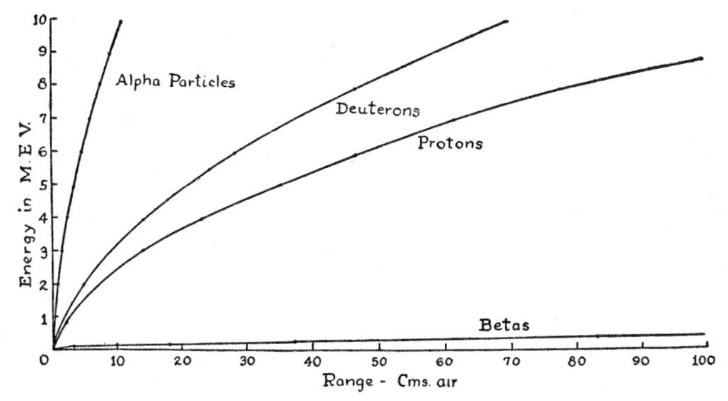

FIG. 4–4. Range-energy relationships for various particles. Range in centimeters of air, energy in million electron volts. (Data from H. A. Bethe, *Revs. Mod. Phys.* 9, 269 (1937))

have measured the efficiencies of alcohol-filled counters and their results confirm the view developed above.

For particles heavier than electrons, the number of ion-pairs produced per cm of path is large. Eq. (4–3) may be used to compute the efficiency of a counter counting alpha particles or protons, but these efficiencies will in almost all cases be unity. The number of ion-pairs produced can be readily computed from the range (see Fig. 4–4) for these particles, recalling that about 35 ev are required to produce each ion-pair.

2. Operation. *a. Introduction.* In this section we propose to discuss the operational characteristics of non-selfquenching Geiger-Mueller counters. We shall consider counters filled with any monatomic or diatomic gas or mixtures thereof. In view of the theory developed above, we shall show what types of operation may be expected, and are actually met in practice. We shall present the characteristic curves and show how these depend on the nature and the pressure of the gas. We shall consider the pulse sizes which are obtained with the various arrangements and the efficiencies of the counters in detecting the radiation of various types. We shall also examine the effects due to negative ions, metastable states, and operation with reversed potentials. The design and construction features and the attached electronic circuits will be discussed in a later chapter.

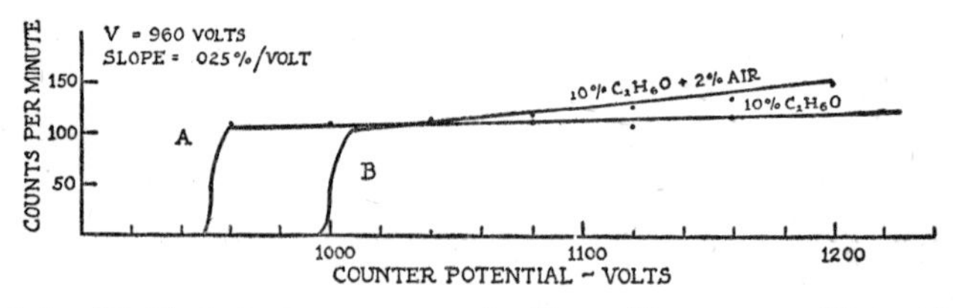

FIG. 4–5. (A) Typical plateau curve of selfquenching counter filled with argon and 10% C_2H_6O vapor. (B) Same counter when 2% air was admitted. Note that starting potential increases and plateau becomes less flat. (Ref. S1)

There are five desirable features which may be realized in counters, to a greater or lesser extent, through proper design. These are (a) low operating potential, (b) long operating voltage range or "plateau," (c) high efficiency, (d) stability with use and time, and (e) pulse size large enough to operate electronic circuits unambiguously. We shall examine the influence of various features on these five desiderata. The purely mechanical features, such as ruggedness, ease of construction and low cost, are discussed in another chapter.

b. Characteristic curves. There are two important characteristic curves exhibited by Geiger counters. The first is the familiar plateau curve, in which the counting rate of a given counter is plotted as a function of voltage, when the gas which it contains and the radiation to which it is exposed are both kept constant. A typical curve of this sort is shown in Fig. 4–5.

These curves are characterized by a rapid rise beyond the starting potential to the Geiger threshold and a more or less flat region beyond this, which is called the plateau. The slope of the plateau and the factors influencing its flatness will be discussed later. At the upper end of the plateau, the counting rate rapidly increases with further rise in voltage, and the counter ceases to be useful for quantitative measurements. This counting rate curve is an integral curve, in which all pulses greater than a certain size are measured. If such a curve shows a flat "plateau," it indicates that, in the region of the plateau, all pulses are of a certain maximum size. A flat plateau may thus be taken to indicate true Geiger counting action, since we have defined this as the process leading to the production of pulses which are all of the same size and independent of the amount of ionization occurring in the initial ionizing event. Moreover, a flat plateau is desirable from an operational viewpoint in that it insures that if the counter be operated somewhere near the middle of the flat portion, the counting rate will be independent of small fluctuations in the operating potential.

The other type of curve which we wish to discuss is that of the starting potential as a function of the pressure of the gas in the counter. Typical curves of this sort are shown in Fig. 4–6. It will be noted that these curves resemble the familiar sparking potential curves and are characterized by a minimum in the neighborhood of a few millimeters and a slow rise toward higher pressures. This rise is practically linear over small changes in pressure. Curves of this sort may be prepared for various kinds of counters and fillings. The rapidly varying portion below one centimeter is of comparatively little significance from the point of view of practical operation, since the efficiency of a counter filled with pressures of 1 cm or less is so small as to make it virtually useless. The usual operating regions for most Geiger counters is in the neighborhood of 7 cm to 20 cm pressure. Operation at still higher pressures is sometimes desirable. To cite cases in which high pressure counters have been found useful, we have those designed by Brown,[B3] in which helium at 1 atm was used, and also the neutron counters,[K5] in which operation at 1 atm and above is desirable from the point of view of efficiency. In the case of helium counters operating at atmospheric pressures, the gas may be flowed into

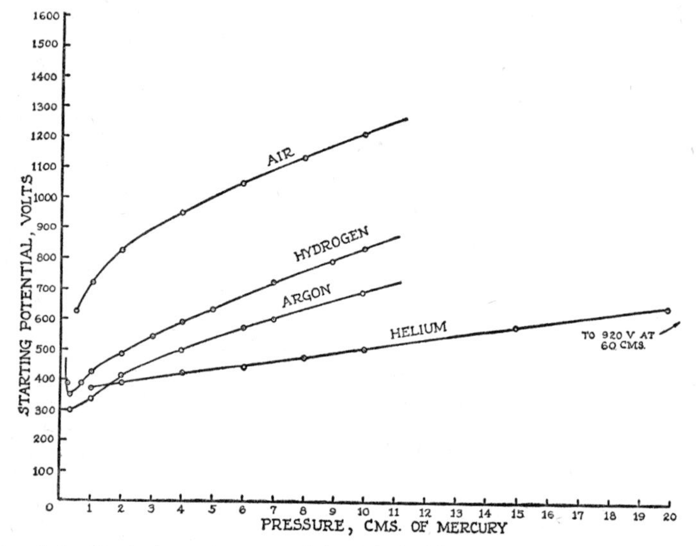

Fig. 4–6. Typical starting potentials with (99%) pure gases. Counter cylinder 1 cm diameter, wire 3 mil. The minimum occurs at about 3 mm. Ordinary operating range 7 to 20 cm. (After C. L. Haines, *Rev. Sci. Inst.* **7**, 411 (1936))

the counter continuously while some portion of it is open to the atmosphere, and the mechanical provisions for introducing a specimen into the volume of the counter are therefore simple. With this arrangement, a radioactive sample to be measured may be introduced into the body of the counter and the radiation emitted in all directions from the substance may be measured.

It is evident from inspection of Fig. 4–6 that the starting potential depends on the nature of the gas. In general, the noble gases produce counters with lower starting potentials than do the common diatomic ones, such as nitrogen or hydrogen. The starting potentials of mixtures will, in general, lie between those of the constituents. Consequently, since a low starting potential is desirable, noble gases have been widely used in counter work.

c. Efficiency. We have shown, in the theoretical discussion, that the efficiency of a counter may be computed from eq. (4–3), and that it depends on the specific ionization of the particle to be counted in the particular gas used in the counter. We have further pointed out that a high efficiency is necessary for good results in most cases. It is comparatively simple to produce a counter with an efficiency of 99.8% or better. The important considerations are the nature of the gas and the pressure. The noble gases, excepting helium, have high specific ionizations, and counters filled to between 7 and 20 cm of such gases will have good efficiencies and low operating potentials.

It is of interest to discuss the case of a counter operating at low efficiency. Counters operating at a low efficiency differ from those operating at a high efficiency in that their operation begins to resemble that of an ionization chamber. As Korff and Danforth have suggested [K6] the exponential for the efficiency—eq. (4–3)—may be expanded and written in terms of its first series member when the exponent is small. Thus the efficiency given by the expression

$$G = 1 - e^{-slp}$$

becomes

$$G = slp. \tag{4–4}$$

Since the efficiency depends on s, the counting rate depends on the size of the ionizing events, and the counter measures a quantity proportional to the total radiation which falls on it, much as does an ionization chamber. A counter of high efficiency counts the number of particles, regardless of the amount of ionization produced by each, whereas one of low efficiency counts particles of high specific ionization preferentially. The counting rate for low efficiencies will be proportional to the volume of the counter while for high efficiencies it is proportional to the cross-sectional area exposed to a flux of radiation. As with an integrating ionization chamber, it is not possible to tell whether a given counting rate with a low efficiency counter is produced by a few particles of high specific ionization or by many with low s. Thus if a counter is exposed to a flux of i ionizing particles per sq cm per sec, and has a cross-sectional area of F sq cm through which the radiation passes, then the counting rate of a high efficiency counter will be iF counts per sec. But for inefficient counters, we must multiply by a value of $G = slp$ less than unity, and since lF is the volume of the counter, which we designate by U, the counting rate will be $ispU$ counts per sec. Thus inefficient counters may have a use in the special case when knowledge of the total radiation is desired, rather than the flux.

Returning to the discussion of counters of high efficiency, the fact that the counting rate depends on the cross-sectional area means that the geometrical relation of the counter and the angular distribution of the radiation must be considered. This is not true for the low-efficiency counters or integrating ionization chambers where the quantity measured depends on the volume of the device and not on its orientation with respect to the particles being measured. Thus for efficient counters, geometrical correction factors are required.

Corrections of this type have been found necessary in the cases in which counters, arranged to cover large sensitive areas, were used for measurement of cosmic radiation.[K6] The cosmic radiation is not incident isotropically on the counter, but falls upon the instruments largely from above. The geometrical corrections are quite sensitive to the angular distribution. Consequently, if the angular distribution varies, as, for example, does that of cosmic radiation as a function of elevation, the intensities at several elevations obtained with electroscopes or ionization chambers cannot be compared with those measured by high-efficiency counters without making the necessary geometrical integrations.

d. Nature and type of gas. (1) *Helium.* Considering first the various monatomic gases, we find that helium has been used by various investigators for filling counters. Counters using helium have been studied extensively by Brown.[B4] Helium has a comparatively low specific ionization, and it is consequently necessary to use a fairly high pressure in order to obtain desirable efficiencies. However, helium counters are also characterized by a low starting potential and therefore comparatively high pressures may be used without encountering excessive operating voltages. One of the features of helium-filled counters is the relative transparency of this gas to radiation in the short-wave regions and the small stopping power which it has for heavy particles.

(2) *Neon and argon.* These two gases are used extensively in counters. Argon, in particular, is inexpensive and has a high specific ionization. Counters with high efficiencies and low starting potentials may readily be made using this gas. Extremely pure argon should be avoided owing to the difficulties which arise due to the metastable states, the effects of which will be discussed below. Ordinary commercial argon, which is often about 98% pure, may be used quite satisfactorily, since the 2% impurity is sufficient to de-excite the metastable states by collision. Krypton and xenon also make excellent gases for counters since both have high specific ionizations and produce low starting potentials. However, expense usually rules them out, and they have, in fact, comparatively little advantage over argon.

(3) *Nitrogen and hydrogen.* Both of these gases are at times used in counters. Each is characterized by a comparatively high starting potential. Hydrogen has an additional disadvantage, namely, a low specific ionization. In order to obtain efficiencies approaching 100% for the detection of beta rays or cosmic rays, considerable pressures of hydrogen are neces-

sary, and the resulting starting potentials may become undesirably high. For example, to obtain an efficiency of 99.8% in a counter with 2 cm average path, the counter would have to be filled to 35 cm of hydrogen and such a counter would require well over 2000 volts for its operating potential.

(4) *Oxygen.* The results obtained with oxygen are somewhat undesirable since in this gas the formation of negative ions is appreciable. The effect of the negative ions will be discussed below.

(5) *Mixtures.* In early experiments, air was used in counters. Air, however, has to a lesser degree the same disadvantage which oxygen has, namely, it permits the formation of a sufficient number of negative ions to produce appreciable spurious counting. In addition, air should be carefully dried in order to remove water vapor which not only may give rise to negative ions, but also may affect the surface of the cathode in time. Mixtures which have been found to be particularly desirable are argon-and-hydrogen or neon-and-hydrogen. In each case, a few percent of hydrogen may be added to the noble gas, and the resulting starting potential is low, almost equal to that due to the noble gas alone, whereas the efficiency is high. The hydrogen molecules remove the energy in the metastable states by collision. Argon-oxygen counters (94% A, 6% O_2) have been studied by the Montgomerys,[M3] and the effects of negative ions were noted.

e. Pulse size. In the theoretical treatment, we showed that the size of the pulse, or in other words, the change in potential of the wire, should be of the order of the overvoltage. That this is indeed frequently the case has been confirmed by numerous investigators. However, in some cases the change in potential of the wire is greater than the overvoltage and the wire drops during the discharge to a value below that necessary for sustaining the discharge. This phenomenon is called "overshooting" and can be produced in any counter by making the capacity attached to the wires small and the overvoltage high.[M3]

If the capacity of the wire system is made high, the counter will ordinarily not overshoot. The phenomenon of overshooting has not been observed by several investigators who sought it, but these observers generally used high capacities on their wire system, and consequently the conditions were not such that the phenomenon would be observed. In Fig. 4–7, a curve of pulse size as a function of overvoltage is shown. In this curve the pulse size would be a straight line for high capacities and departs from a straight line in the direction of pulses larger than the overvoltage at high overvoltages. The experimental data are taken from the observations made by the Montgomerys.[M3]

The values of q, the charge collected on the central wire, are closely related to the pulse size. Several observers have measured the charge collected, notably Stever and Ramsey.[S3, R5] One simple procedure for measuring q is to arrange a high-resistance, low-leakage condenser to supply the counter voltage, and then to measure the potential change dV of this condenser after an assigned number of counts n have taken place. The charge q then will equal $nCdV$, where C is the capacity of the condenser. The charge q collected during a pulse was found to be proportional to the overvoltage. It is found to increase somewhat when overshooting takes place. The charge collected is of the order of 10×10^{-6} microcoulombs per volt of overvoltage for small pulse sizes and may run to 100 times this value for larger pulses.

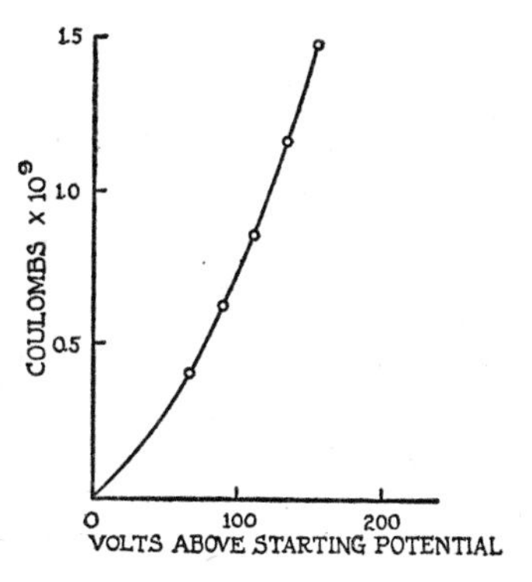

FIG. 4–7. The amount of charge formed in a counter which overshoots, as a function of the potential above the starting potential applied to it. (C. G. and D. D. Montgomery, *Phys. Rev.* **57**, 1034 (1940))

f. Effects due to negative ions. Let us consider the effects due to negative ions. Suppose that a negative ion is formed within the active volume of the counter during the discharge. Accelerated by the field, this ion will drift toward the central wire. The mobility of negative ions is the same in order of magnitude as that of positive ions, and the negative ion will therefore require a few times 10^{-4} second to cross the dimensions of an average counter. Such negative ions may then arrive in the high field region next to the wire after the Townsend avalanche is over and after the positive ion space charge sheath has progressed far enough toward the cylinder, so that the field near the wire has partly recovered to its normal value. The negative ion entering the high field region may lose its electron in the immediate neighborhood of the wire, due to the high field. In this case the electron which is thus freed will start a new avalanche and produce a new count. Alternatively, the negative ion may produce ionization by collision in the neighborhood of the wire and may again thus start a new Townsend avalanche. Since recovery from the first count has partially taken place, the counter would then register a new count. There is therefore the possibility that the counter will discharge at times subsequent to the completion of the initial count, if negative ions are formed within a counter. In other words, spurious counts or an excessive number of close doubles or multiples may be produced by negative ions.

The probability of the formation of a negative ion in the counter subsequent to the discharge may be calculated from the known electron attachment coefficient. The electron attachment coefficient for various gases may be taken from the tables given by Compton and Langmuir.[C2] Numerical values are presented in Table 4–2. The coefficient is defined as the number of collisions which an electron must make with neutral molecules or atoms before it sticks and forms a negative ion. An electron will make approximately 10^5 collisions in crossing a counter, the mean free path depending on the pressure. Therefore, if this coefficient exceeds 10^5, there will be a very small probability that any negative ions will be formed, since the electrons will not have made enough collisions before they are collected. The values reported for the coefficient are high for Argon, H_2, N_2, and ammonia. The value for air is 2×10^5, which is close to the critical value of 10^5, mentioned above, but the figure for O_2 and for H_2O and Cl_2 are all less than this criti-

TABLE 4–2. ELECTRON ATTACHMENT COEFFICIENT *

Gas	n	N
CO	1.6×10^8	2.2×10^{11}
NH_3	9.9×10^7	2.9×10^{11}
C_2H_6	2.5×10^6	4.8×10^{11}
N_2O	6.1×10^5	3.36×10^{11}
Air	2.0×10^5	2.17×10^{11}
O_2, H_2O	4×10^4	$2.06, 2.83 \times 10^{11}$
Cl_2	$<2 \times 10^3$	4.50×10^{11}

* Here n represents the average number of electron impacts which result in one attachment to form a negative ion, and N the number of electron impacts per sec against gas molecules. Data from Compton and Langmuir, *Revs. Mod. Phys.*, **2**, 193 (1930).

cal value. Hence, negative ions will be formed in sufficient numbers to produce significant effects only in the case of oxygen, water, and the halogens. It will be recalled that iodine was used in some counters in the early days. It is evident that this gas and others in that family are undesirable in counters, because of the high electron attachment probability. Water vapor and other similar compounds should also be avoided on this ground.

g. Effects due to metastable states. Suppose an atom is left in a metastable state as a result of a discharge. The atom will then remain in this state until radiation takes place, or a collision of the second kind occurs and the energy of the metastable state is transferred into kinetic energy. Metastable states occur in the noble gases. In pure argon, for example, metastable atoms may form in the discharge. The lifetime of these metastable states, before radiation takes place, is of the order of 10^{-4} sec or longer. Atoms in metastable states are not affected by the field and drift about within the volume of a counter. Such atoms may collide with the walls of the counter while they are in the metastable state, or (less probably) they may radiate. Either process can give rise to a secondary electron. If such secondary electrons are produced after the positive ion sheath has traversed a substantial fraction of the radius of the counter, a new count will occur. In the new discharge, new metastable atoms are presumably formed, and if these metastable states in turn produce still more secondary electrons, then the discharge in the counter does not terminate. It is for this reason that pure noble gases are not desirable in counters and a foreign gas should be used which de-excites the metastable states by collision. Thus, for example, the addition of a few percent of hydrogen to a counter filled with pure argon insures that a collision between argon and hydrogen molecules will take place within a time short compared to the lifetime of the metastable state, and therefore will result in the elimination of the metastable atoms.

h. Operation of a counter with reversed potential. If the potential on the counter is reversed and the wire is made negative with respect to the cylinder, the counter may still be made to operate as a Geiger counter. The detailed description of the discharge mechanism will, however, be quite different. An electron avalanche will be formed, but the electrons will proceed outward toward the cylinder. Since the electrons move into regions in which the field becomes progressively weaker, the avalanche which they produce will tend to taper off, and the multiplicative process will decrease as the electrons travel outward. The positive ions, on the other hand, may enter the regions of field so high that in one mean free path they acquire enough energy to produce ionization by collision. Additional electrons are thus produced as the ions travel inwards toward the central wire. These electrons will travel out to the cylinder, where they are collected. If they produce additional electrons by bombardment of the cylinder, these electrons are also collected on the cylinder and do not contribute to the continuation of the discharge. The positive ions, however, arrive on the wire and others may produce avalanches at times comparatively long after the electrons have been collected. Thus a count may take place immediately after the ionizing event which caused it, or there may be a considerable time which elapses, depending on whether the initial ion was formed near the wire or far from it. Such random time intervals between the occurrence of the initial ionizing event and the count are called statistical time-lags. Counters with potentials reversed will therefore, in general, show large statistical time-lags. Further, since not all the positives arrive at once, they will also show considerable fluctuations in the size and shape of the pulse. Because of the time-lags, they are of no value in coincidence circuits,[C4] since any effective coincidence-counting arrangement assumes minimum time-lag. The voltage region in which such counters may be expected to give reliable results is comparatively small and the plateaus are not at all flat.

i. Experiments on counters with potential-reversing circuits. Since the fundamental limitation on the recovery time of counters is due to the mobility of the positive ions, it has occurred to many observers independently to attempt to collect these ions rapidly near the place where they are produced. The first successful experiments along this line to be reported in the literature were made by Simpson [S4] who employed a square-wave generator (multivibrator) circuit to apply a reverse potential to the counter. If a count takes place in a counter, the positive ion sheath is formed in the immediate vicinity of the center wire. The electron avalanche is complete before the positive ions have moved any appreciable distance. If this arrival of electrons on the wire can trigger a circuit which now rapidly makes the center wire negative and cylinder positive, the positive ions in the counter could travel the much shorter distance to the central wire and there be neutralized. This action would speed up the operation of the counter.

In Simpson's experiment, this was done and a circuit was developed for the purpose. The requirements to be met by such a circuit are quite severe. If the counter normally operates with the wire 1500 volts more positive than the cylinder, it would be necessary to make it several hundred volts more negative than the cylinder, keep it at that potential for a time long enough to collect the positives, and then return it to its original state, all in a time short compared to the travel time of the positives across the counter, i.e., less than 10^{-4} sec. It is therefore necessary to apply a square pulse, 1800 volts or more in amplitude and a few microseconds in duration, to the wire. Most receiving tubes will fail under such operation, and Simpson employed a transmitting tube of type 807. This tube was driven by a trigger circuit, which was in turn actuated by the small pulse due to the electrons arriving on the center wire. Elaborate precautions had to be taken to insure that the final pulse would be really square, eliminating rounded corners and tails to the pulse, and rendering the trigger circuit insensitive during the cycle of operation. A detailed discussion of the circuit is out of place here, and the reader is referred to the original paper.[84] It will suffice to say that the operation was successful, and that it was possible to collect the positive ions in a short time. Simpson reported that the operation could be carried out and the counter restored to a sensitive condition in times of the order of 2×10^{-5} sec, with "no indication that the limit had been reached." Although this circuit is probably not, at the present time, readily adaptable to general laboratory use, it appears probable that future developments in high speed counters will make use of this principle. Circuits of this type will no doubt be simplified and become part of standard laboratory practice. The success of this experiment points the way to important new developments in counter technique and suggests many interesting and significant fields of study. An order of magnitude has already been gained and further progress seems probable.

j. Intrinsic time lags. Most discussions of Geiger counters assume that the count takes place immediately after the ionizing event occurs. It is well to consider this assumption rather carefully, especially if use is to be made of extremely short resolving times. As we have indicated above, once an electron starts to produce an avalanche the action takes place very quickly, and in less than a microsecond the avalance is over, electrons have been collected and the positive ion space charge sheath has been produced. The electrons, wherever formed, can traverse the dimensions of the counter in less than a microsecond. It was therefore somewhat surprising when various observers reported evidence that a counter did not discharge until some time several microseconds after the primary ionizing event had occurred. The Montgomerys [M7] have given a good explanation of this effect.

The intrinsic time-lag in the counter is attributed to the formation of negative ions. If the electron, formed in a primary ionizing event at some point distant from the wire, is captured to form a negative ion while it travels toward the wire, its speed of travel will be much reduced. Taking the mobility of a small negative ion at about 1.5 cm per sec per volt per cm, a negative ion will travel in a field of 10^3 volts per cm and 0.1 atm pressure, at roughly 1.5×10^4 cm per sec and hence would require many microseconds to traverse a counter. This time would be considerably reduced if the electron were captured near the wire, as it would have traversed most of the distance at the much higher speeds characteristic of an electron, and would complete its journey to the wire faster because it was in the high-field region. The time still would be appreciable compared to that required for the electron to complete its journey in the absence of capture. It is further to be noted that the experiments in which these lags were observed used counters in which oxygen was present as a constituent in an amount of 6%. If short resolving times are to be used, the formation of negative ions must be avoided. This is particularly important in coincidence experiments where a lag of several microseconds may produce an apparent inefficiency in a fast circuit.

k. The use of grids in counters. Experiments have been reported by Korff and Ramsey [K11] and W. F. Libby [L5] in which a grid was introduced into a counter. The cylinder of the counter was 5.6 cm in diameter and a grid of 1 cm diameter was arranged around the central wire. Since the avalanche mechanism occurs only in the immediate vicinity of the wire, the position of the grid does not affect the avalanche. The pulse size is controlled by the potential difference between the grid and the central wire.

When the outer cylinder is made negative with respect to the grid, any electrons produced in the outer space are accelerated toward the grid. Disregarding the few which are collected on the grid, most electrons pass through the grid and produce counts as though the grid were not there. Only a small potential difference between grid and cylinder is necessary. Potential differences of as little as 10 volts were found to serve. Increasing this potential difference to 200 volts made no detectable difference, as the outer region is merely an ion-collecting zone. If the potential was reversed, and the grid made negative by 10 volts with respect to the cylinder, the outer volume ceased to contribute electrons to the discharge and the counter acted as though it were one whose diameter was equal to that of the grid. Varying the magnitude of the grid-cathode potential difference again had no effect.

When the potential difference between grid and cylinder was made zero, the counter went into a continuous discharge. The explanation of this is that any electrons produced in the field free space between grid and cylinder might then drift about and at random times drift through the grid. As soon as each one has passed through the grid it starts a count. A rapid succession of counts at random intervals is the equivalent of a continuous discharge.

The advantages of using the grid are (a) that the total operating voltage of the counter can be reduced and (b) that the resolving time is shortened since the positives cease to influence the discharge as soon as they have reached the grid and thus have only had to travel over one-fifth (in this case) of the radius of the cylinder. The disadvantages are (a) increased complexity in construction and (b) a few electrons are collected on the grid. As to the operating voltage, with a small diameter grid only that voltage needed for a small-diameter counter need be used, plus a grid-plate potential difference of 10 or 22½ or some other convenient low voltage. For a large diameter cylinder, the attainable voltage reductions are quite considerable. This consideration is, for example, of great importance in saving weight in cosmic-ray-balloon experiments.

B. Selfquenching Counters

1. Introduction. In this section we shall discuss counters containing polyatomic gases or vapors. "Polyatomic" we shall use to describe a molecule consisting of four or more atoms. Triatomic molecules will constitute a special case separately discussed below. The counters in question may have monatomic or diatomic gases added. The monatomic component may often be the largest fraction percentage-wise, as for example in counters filled with 90% argon plus 10% alcohol vapor. The polyatomic molecule, however, if present in appreciable amounts, affects the character of the discharge to such an extent that the operation of the counter is entirely different from the non-selfquenching type of counter discussed previously.

It was reported by Trost [T2] in 1937 that the addition of a certain amount of the vapor of some organic compounds caused the counter discharge to "quench" itself, in other words to terminate due to some internal mechanism in the discharge. This property permitted the elimination of the "quenching resistance" or the equivalent electronic circuit. Since the high resistance was the chief cause of the slow recovery time of the non-selfquenching counter, the selfquenching counters exhibited an apparently much shorter recovery time and hence became known as "fast" counters. As we shall show, this is a misnomer, because the actual time required by the "fast" counter to complete one cycle of its discharge mechanism is longer than that for the "slow" or non-selfquenching counter. We shall therefore use the term "selfquenching" when referring to these counters as this more nearly describes their properties.

Since Trost's early experiments, various observers have tried a large number of different compounds in counters. The result of these experiments may be summarized by saying that any polyatomic (gas) molecule will produce the "quenching" action. The molecule need not be organic, BF_3 being an illustration of a non-organic molecule which causes quenching, although most polyatomic molecules are organic. There does not appear to be any great difference in merit between various possible polyatomic molecules, each having certain advantages and disadvantages as compared to others. For example, amyl acetate shows a somewhat longer useful life but a slower resolving-time than does methane. We shall discuss these various properties below.

In selecting a gas for a selfquenching counter we consider the following desiderata: (1) The counter should have high efficiency; (2) it should have a short resolving time; (3) it should have a wide plateau; (4) it should have a flat plateau; (5) it should have a minimum temperature coefficient and (6) it should have a long life. A low operating potential and ease of construction are desirable considerations which we shall also mention. The optimum amount of polyatomic constituent to be added to a monatomic or diatomic gas will be described, as well as the minimum amount needed to produce quenching. In order to understand why a given combination of factors is desirable, we must consider the atomic mechanism of the discharge.

2. Theory. In 1942, Stever [S3] extended the analysis which the Montgomerys [M3] had originally prepared regarding non-selfquenching counters, to selfquenching counters. The Montgomerys pointed out that one of the important differences between the non-selfquenching and selfquenching counters was that when the positive ions formed in the avalanche reached the cylinder, secondary electrons were formed. These electrons caused the discharge to continue indefinitely in the case of the non-selfquenching counter while in the selfquenching type, these secondary electrons were absent. Korff and Present [K7] in 1944 proposed a mechanism to explain the absence of secondary electrons. Stever discussed the formation of the space charge sheath, following the Montgomery theory, and showed how the measured dead times and recovery times depended on the motion of this sheath.

To understand this operation, let us consider the definitions and meaning of the dead time and recovery time of a counter. Suppose a count occurs. There will follow an insensitive time, while the discharge mechanism is operating, during which time, if another ionizing event occurs in the counter, it is not detected. This time is defined as the dead time. At the end of the dead time if an ionizing event should occur, a pulse so small that it can just be detected, would be observed. If the event takes place a trifle later, the pulse will be larger, and finally a time will come when the pulse will be of full height. The recovery time is then defined as the time required by the counter to recover so that a pulse following another by this interval shall be of full size. Stever devised an electronic circuit to demonstrate this phenomenon on an oscilloscope screen and Fig. 4–8 shows a sketch of the pattern seen. The dead time and recovery time are indicated in the figure.

Stever discusses the dead time and recovery time in terms of the movement of the positive ion sheath. This analysis has already been discussed in the section on non-selfquenching counters, since Stever's treatment is substantially the same as the Montgomerys'. The dead time is understood as the time

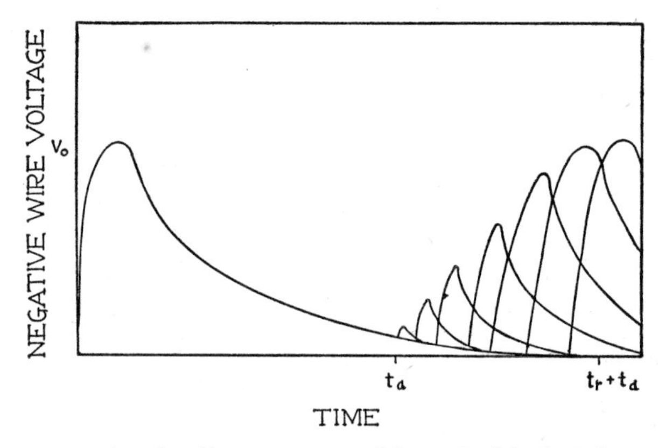

FIG. 4–8. Drawing of oscilloscope pattern of the result of the dead-time experiment. This shows the dead time t_d and the recovery time t_r. The time $(t_d + t_r)$ corresponds to the arrival of the positive ion sheath at the cylinder. The time t_d corresponds to the point in the transit of the positive ions at which the field about the wire has returned to threshold field. (From H. G. Stever, *Phys. Rev.* **61**, 40 (1940))

required for the space charge sheath to move out to a distance such that the field near the wire will have recovered to such a value that counts will again be observed. In other words, as when the space charge sheath is first formed, the field inside the sheath decreases below the value necessary to sustain an avalanche, i.e., below the Geiger threshold. As the sheath moves out, the field between the sheath and the wire increases and returns to normal. Stever shows that the "critical radius" r_c is related to the overvoltage V and the cylinder radius r by the relation

$$r_c = r^{-V/2q} \tag{4–5}$$

where q is the positive ion space charge per unit length. The dead time is the time required by the positive ions to move out to r_c.

As the positives continue past R toward the cylinder, the field near the wire recovers to normal. The recovery time is the time required by the ions to reach the cylinder and be neutralized. The dead and recovery times are therefore determined by the mobility of the positive ions. This drift velocity dx/dt of an ion in a field E at pressure P is determined by the field, and may be written

$$dx/dt = kE/p \tag{4–6}$$

where k is a constant called the "mobility," and dx is the distance moved by the ion in time dt. The quantity k is usually expressed in cm per sec per volt per cm at atmospheric pressure [cf. eq. (2–2)].

Numerical values of k have been determined by many observers for various types of ions moving in various gases. The numerical values of k and the fields used in counters are such that about 10^{-4} sec is required for the ions to reach the cylinder. The order-of-magnitude agreement between this figure and the known recovery times has been commented on by the Montgomerys and others and has been used to support arguments regarding the natural insensitive time. The case of the selfquenching counter is somewhat complicated since two kinds of ions are often present, those of argon and those of ethyl alcohol, for example. The mobility of argon ions in argon is more accurately known than the mobility of the mixtures in mixed gases. It is therefore not possible simply by referring to values of k in tables, to answer the problem completely. Electron transfer, as we shall show, somewhat simplifies the picture.

The form of the dependence of k on E and on p, the pressure, is complicated, and has been studied in detail by Loeb [L1] and others. Near the wire, where the field is high, k is not constant. Moreover the functional relationship varies considerably from gas to gas. If k is assumed constant, the dead time can be calculated, but experiments do not confirm the values so obtained. The recovery time can be calculated with some degree of success, since most of the travel time of the ions is spent in the low field regions where k may be assumed constant. The expression for the recovery time, t_r, is readily derived from eqs. (4–5 and 4–6) recalling that the voltage $V = \int Edr$, and is found to be

$$t_r = \frac{(r^2 - r_c^2) \log (r/r_w)}{2kC} \tag{4–7}$$

where r_w and r are the wire and cylinder radii. The observed values of t_r lie between 1.0 and 2.2×10^{-4} sec for counters operating at between 950 and 1450 volts, $r_w = 0.01$ cm, $r = 1.11$ cm, $r_c = 0.65$ cm and filled to between 5 and 14 cm pressure of a 90% argon + 10% Xylol mixture. The values predicted by eq. (4–7) are generally within 20% of the observed figures. This agreement must be regarded as satisfactory in view of the uncertainties in the problem, the lack of precision in consideration of the exact meaning of the mobility, and the effects of electron transfer which we shall discuss below.

The dead times and recovery times have been measured by Stever [S3] for a variety of different gases and mixtures and a few typical ones are listed in Table 4–3. It will be seen that the dead times and recovery times are of the stated order of magnitude, 1 to 2×10^{-4} sec, for the lighter gases, and somewhat higher, up to 8×10^{-4} sec, for the heavier vapors. This is to be expected since the mobilities of the heavy ions are less than that of the light ions.

Eq. (4–7) and the arguments regarding the dead time and recovery time all assume that the discharge spreads along the wire of the counter. A number of experiments have been performed which support this view. Since these experiments also have a bearing on the actual mechanism of the counter discharge, we shall now describe them.

TABLE 4–3. OBSERVED DEAD TIMES AND RECOVERY TIMES

Gases	Total Pressure, Cm	Dead Time, Seconds	Recovery Time, Seconds	Reference
95% argon, 5% xylol	13.4	2.6×10^{-4}	4.3×10^{-4}	S3
95% argon, 5% xylol	11.0	2.4×10^{-4}	4.3×10^{-4}	S3
95% argon, 5% xylol	9.0	2.1×10^{-4}	3.7×10^{-4}	S3
95% argon, 5% xylol	7.0	1.8×10^{-4}	3.6×10^{-4}	S3
94.5% argon, 5.5% ethyl alcohol	10.1	1.4×10^{-4}	2.3×10^{-4}	S7
80% argon, 20% alcohol	10.0	2.1×10^{-4}	2.3×10^{-4}	S7
67% argon, 33% alcohol	9.7	2.2×10^{-4}	2.45×10^{-4}	S7
94.8% argon, 5.2% amyl acetate	15.0	2.0×10^{-4}	4.0×10^{-4}	S7
90.9% argon, 9.1% amyl acetate	15.0	2.0×10^{-4}	4.0×10^{-4}	S7
94.8% argon, 5.2% amyl acetate	15.0	2.8×10^{-4}	4.8×10^{-4}	S7

First we will recall the early and unpublished experiments, made by Ramsey, Brode and others, in which two counters (*A* and *B*) were so arranged that the inside region of one counter could "see" the inside of the other. In other words, photons or electrons could pass unobstructed from the region near the wire of one counter to a similar region or could reach the inside of the cathode of the other. The result of these experiments was that when counter *A* discharged, counter *B* discharged each time the two were filled with non-selfquenching gases or mixtures. When the counters were filled with selfquenching mixtures, counter *B* discharged only in a random relation to the discharges of *A*. By applying a magnetic field which would have so deflected electrons that they could not have reached the other counter, Ramsey further showed that what passed between the counters was photons.

A further extension of this experiment was reported by Stever, who divided the wire of a counter with a small glass bead. He found again that a bead would stop the spread of the discharge in a selfquenching counter and not in a non-selfquenching one. The single counter, with a bead on the center of the central wire, was thus effectively turned into two counters. Either section would discharge independently but would not cause the other to discharge. He then found that a continuous wire might pass through the bead and that the bead would still stop the spread of the discharge. On the other hand, when the cylinder was divided but the wire was continuous the discharge spread into both sections. In other words, the discharge spreads in a narrow sheath along the wire.

The minimum size of the bead necessary to interrupt the discharge was then sought. This size, it was found, depended on the gas pressure and the overvoltage. Thus, for example, a 0.022 in. diameter bead on an 0.008 in. diameter wire stopped the discharge at 10 cm pressure and 1300 volts; but, at 3.5 cm pressure, above 840 volts the discharge was able to pass the bead, while between 840 and the threshold at 790 the bead stopped the spread.

Wilkening and Kanne [W2] made a similar test, with an obstruction (in this case a small quartz disk) on the wire and studied the minimum amount of alcohol vapor which had to be added to an argon-filled counter to prevent the discharge from spreading across the disk. They found that if less than 5% of alcohol vapor were added, the discharge often spread across the obstruction. They further found that the spreading was more likely to occur if the overvoltage was greater. As the processes are statistical in nature, there is no one voltage or pressure at which the spread sets in abruptly. But, if, for example, the voltage is raised, more and more discharges will spread over into the next section.

We are now in a position to inquire into the mechanism of quenching, or in other words to consider the effects produced by the polyatomic molecules. We shall follow the discussions of this problem given by Korff and Present.[K7] It will be shown that the characteristic property of the polyatomic molecule which is important for the operation of a counter is the short lifetime of the excited electronic states against predissociation, i.e., polyatomic molecules, having absorbed a quantum, usually predissociate before they have an opportunity to lose the absorbed energy by radiation. Atoms and diatomic molecules, on the other hand, generally reradiate the energy which they have absorbed.

The excited electronic states of a diatomic molecule have sharp rotational levels well above the dissociation energy of the molecule, and predissociation is only an occasional phenomenon. In polyatomic molecules containing four or more atoms, predissociation is the rule rather than the exception, and the absorption spectrum in the ultraviolet shows diffuse absorption bands with the rotational structure obliterated, as well as regions of continuous absorption. This is essentially due to the opportunities for "crossing over" provided by the many intersections of the potential energy hypersurfaces extending over a wide range of energies. The heavier the molecule, the more diffuse is the spectrum and the more likely is predissociation. Light polyatomic molecules present an intermediate case, and the spectroscopy and photochemistry of each must be considered separately to determine the probable result of a given excitation.

In our definitions, Chapter 1, we have defined "quenching" as any process causing the discharge to terminate. There are three distinct types of "quenching" involved in the operation of a selfquenching counter: (a) quenching of photons in the initial avalanche, (b) electrostatic quenching of the avalanche by the positive ion space charge, and (c) quenching of the secondary emission when the positive ions reach the cathode. The quenching of the discharge involves both the electrostatic quenching and the quenching of secondary emission. We propose to discuss the rôle of the polyatomic gas in quenching cases (a) and (c), since (b) has already been covered.

First let us examine the rôle of the polyatomic gas in the initial avalanche. Common polyatomic constituents of counters are methane and alcohol vapor. Let us consider an argon-methane counter operating in the "proportional" region, in which the size of the pulse is proportional to the number of ions formed in the initial ionizing event. A theory of the formation of the avalanche in this case has been given by Rose and Korff. Assuming that the electrons multiply by collision and that photoelectrons do not contribute to the avalanche, they obtain a formula for the gas amplification which agrees well with experiment as long as a sufficient amount of methane is present in the counter. When the relative or absolute amount of methane is reduced too far, the gas amplification is found to rise more steeply with increasing voltage than predicted by the formula, thus indicating an additional source of electrons. The dependence of this effect on the nature of the cathode surface led Rose and Korff to suggest that photoelectrons from the cathode were contributing to the avalanche. When the counter voltage was raised sufficiently, all the curves deviated from the values predicted by the formula.

They also suggested that collisions which cause electronic excitation of the polyatomic molecule will usually result in decomposition rather than in photon emission. This is in agreement with other evidence to be discussed below, and is supported by experiments of Glockler [G6] in which electrons with 17-ev energy introduced into a methane-filled photo-cell produced no measurable photoelectric current. We wish to emphasize here that in a counter containing a mixture of gases the principal rôle of the polyatomic gas in the avalanche is to absorb the ultraviolet photons emitted by the inert gas (argon). Many photons originate in the avalanche from excited argon atoms. Ranging in energy from 11.5 to 15.7 ev, these photons would liberate electrons from the cathode (photoelectric threshold about 4 ev), were they not absorbed in the gas. Since a gas mixture containing 50% argon to 50% ether shows no evidence of cathode effect, the argon photons must be absorbed by ether molecules before they reach the cathode. This is also in accord with Ramsey's double-counter experiment, cited above, in which it was shown that when counter *A* discharged, if the photons from this discharge could reach the interior of counter *B*, then counter *B* discharged every time if the two were filled with a non-quenching gas (argon), and only at random times if the two were filled with a quenching gas (alcohol).

We inquire next into the details of the absorption act. When a molecule absorbs an ultraviolet photon and passes into an excited electronic state, there are several possible competitive modes of de-excitation: (1) decomposition (dissociation or predissociation), (2) radiation (fluorescence), and (3) deactivation by collision. Process (3) cannot occur in less than 10^{-8} sec, which is the collision time in an ordinary counter. Process (2) involves a radiation lifetime of 10^{-8} sec. Process (1), when possible, occurs within 10^{-11} to 10^{-13} sec, depending on the breadth of the levels. If the rotational structure is obliterated, the lifetime is about 100 times longer than if the vibrational structure is obliterated (continuous absorption). Diatomic molecules, in general, as well as certain light polyatomic molecules, possess stable electronic states with well defined vibrational-rotational structure well above the dissociation limit or limits of the molecule. Excitation of the molecule into this region of energy results in re-emission of the absorbed photon or fluorescence and only rarely in dissociation. Hence, the photons produced in the discharge would not be quenched by a diatomic gas. On the other hand, if we examine the spectroscopic and photochemical data for methane, ammonia, and other gases used in fast counters for which data are available,[R6] we can understand why these gases are photon-quenching. The photo-decomposition of methane in the ultraviolet is well known and the absorption spectrum, taken at a pressure of 1 mm of mercury, shows continuous absorption from 1560 Å down to at least 850 Å, the limit of observation. The ultraviolet photons emitted by excited argon atoms range from 1070 Å to 790 Å; hence they are quenched by methane. Ammonia vapor also photodecomposes in the ultraviolet and the spectrum shows continuous absorption below 1200 Å. Hence ammonia also quenches the argon photons.

Evidence of the decomposition of the alcohol vapor in a fast counter has been obtained by Spatz.[S1] Decomposition in the initial avalanche is to be attributed partly to electron impact and partly to photo-dissociation. As we shall see later, further decomposition occurs when the alcohol ions reach the cathode. The primary decomposition products are usually free radicals which combine to form a miscellaneous assortment of organic molecules. Some of these decomposition products will be quenching gases. However, with continued use of the counter, all of the larger vapor molecules are broken up and the end products of the decomposition are a non-quenching gas, such as hydrogen or oxygen, and heavy hydrocarbons deposited on the walls. These considerations explain why selfquenching counters "go bad" with continued use. Since about 10^{10} alcohol ions are decomposed at the cathode in each discharge, as will be explained in the next section, and since there are altogether about 10^{20} alcohol molecules in the counter, the counter will go bad after about 10^{10} counts. This is in accord with Spatz's observations. These considerations further explain why a methane counter has a shorter life than an alcohol counter. Methane is already far down the list of decomposition products of alcohol and itself can decompose only once or twice before it is reduced to non-quenching diatomic molecules. We can also understand why a greater proportion of methane than alcohol must be added to argon to produce a selfquenching counter. This is due partly to the greater number of vibration-rotation levels available for inelastic electron impacts in the case of the alcohol molecule and partly to the higher quantum yield of the photo-decomposition of alcohol.

Some of the results of Wilkening and Kanne cited above on localization of the discharge will be examined next. The discharge in the Geiger region normally spreads the entire length of the wire in both non-selfquenching and selfquenching counters. A reduction in the field near the central wire by some artificial means, such as the presence of an insulating bead, will interrupt the spread of the discharge in a fast counter but not in a slow counter. In the latter case, photoelectrons from the cathode spread the discharge beyond the obstacle. Wilkening and Kanne used various devices to interrupt the spread of the discharge and measured the effectiveness of the localizing devices in various gases. Selfquenching counters showed 100% "localization." However, a mixture of 1 cm of methane with 9 cm of argon showed only a 50% localization. This is consistent with the fact that the photon-quenching is incomplete in this case, as we may verify from the gas amplification curves given by Rose and Korff. At 10-cm pressure even a 50% argon-methane mixture shows evidence of appreciable photo-effect. Counters filled with monatomic and diatomic gases showed "zero localization," or complete spread of the discharge, corresponding to the total absence of photon-quenching.

We should expect a close correlation between the extent of localization and the length of the proportional region. It has been reported by Korff [K4] and others that selfquenching counters have a much longer proportional region than slow counters at the same total pressure. This is a consequence of the more rapid rise of the amplification factor of a non-selfquenching counter with increasing voltage, which is in turn due to the photoelectric effect at the cathode. Thus the spreading of the discharge beyond an obstacle and the rapid rise of the amplification factor are due to the same cause: photons in the avalanche. The counters found by Wilkening and Kanne to show

100% localization are all counters containing heavy polyatomic vapors which are present in sufficient amount to absorb the argon photons. The methane-argon counter showing 50% localization has a short proportional region. Counters filled with diatomic gases go over directly into a continuous discharge with very short proportional regions, seldom characterized by values of the gas amplification as great as 100 before instability sets in, and such counters show zero localization.

Consider next the transition from the proportional region to the Geiger region in which the size of the pulse is independent of the number of ions formed in the initial ionizing event. At the threshold voltage of the Geiger region, the amplification factor theoretically rises to infinity; in practice the Geiger threshold corresponds to an amplification factor between 10^8 and 10^{12}. Let us assume that the counter has a negligible resistance in series with it. When the Geiger threshold is reached, a non-selfquenching counter will go into a "continuous" discharge, whereas a selfquenching counter will give a single sharp pulse. Because of the absence of resistance, the counter is at its operating potential during the entire time that the positive ions are moving out to the cathode. The electric field in the vicinity of the wire is below the threshold field until the ions have moved out to Stever's "critical distance." The positive ions then have drift velocities of the order of one-tenth their thermal velocities and the kinetic energy they acquire between collisions is less than 0.1 ev. Thus they can neither excite nor ionize, so that if no further ionizing particles enter the counter nothing happens until the ions reach the cathode and are neutralized. It is at this juncture that the behavior of an argon-filled counter differs from that of a methane-filled counter. Secondary electron emission takes place in the argon counter and, since the counter is at operating potential at this time, the entire cycle is repeated. Thus the discharge in a non-selfquenching counter is self-perpetuating although the avalanches are intermittent. In a methane counter, on the other hand, the discharge terminates when the methane ions are neutralized and no secondary emission can occur because, instead of radiating, the methane decomposes upon neutralization.

Details of the neutralization act and subsequent secondary emission will be considered next. When an argon ion approaches to within 10^{-7} cm of the cathode surface, the field of the ion becomes great enough to extract an electron from the metal. This phenomenon of field emisssion is well known and is substantially the same as that which occurs when a high field is applied between electrodes. In the language of quantum mechanics, the electrons in the metal are separated from the vacant energy-levels in the ion by a potential barrier at the metal surface. Quantum mechanical procedures permit calculation of the probability of an electron from the metal "leaking" through the barrier and neutralizing the ion. The electrons in the metal are at a level of ϕ volts below the top of the barrier, where ϕ is the work function. The vacant levels in the ion are at I volts below the top of the barrier, where I is the ionization potential. The difference in energy which the neutralized atom must radiate is $(I - \phi)$ volts approximately, the exact value depending on the location of excitation levels in the atom. In the case of argon ions and a copper cathode, the neutralized atoms are formed in the excited state at 11.5 ev. The distance of approach at which the probability of neutralization approaches unity has been calculated by Oliphant and Moon,[01] using the Fowler-Nordheim formula. The probability of neutralization is an extremely sensitive function of the distance. For ions of thermal velocities approaching a copper surface the critical distance is about 5×10^{-8} cm. Thus the neutralization must take place before the ions are 5×10^{-8} cm from the wall, after which the neutralized atoms reach the wall in about 2×10^{-12} sec. Many atoms, however, do not reach the wall since the momentum communicated to the ion on neutralization is of the same order of magnitude as its initial thermal momentum.

It has been found experimentally that He+ ions which collide with an outgassed platinum surface at a glancing angle escape largely as neutral atoms in the metastable state. This indicates that an ion may be neutralized without making an inelastic collision with the wall. Many neutralized atoms, however, will approach the surface closely enough to transfer their excitation energy to an electron in the metal, resulting in the emission of a secondary electron if $I > 2\phi$. Another way of putting this is to say that, if the ionization potential is greater than twice the work function, then on the average two electrons will be pulled out of the metal, one of which neutralizes the ion and the other becomes a secondary electron forthwith. The probability of secondary emission by an excited atom approaching the surface has been calculated by Massey.[M4] According to Massey's formula, an atom of thermal velocity must approach to within 2×10^{-8} cm of the surface to make secondary emission probable, i.e., the wave functions of the atomic and metallic electrons must overlap. Since the radiation lifetime of the excited state of argon formed on neutralization is 10^{-7} sec, many of the argon atoms will liberate electrons from the cathode.

Suppose a methane ion captures an electron from the wall. The ionization energy of methane is 14.5 ev, and the neutralized molecule therefore has the same excitation as a molecule which has absorbed light of wave-length 1200 Å. The spectrum of methane, as has been previously mentioned, shows continuous absorption below 1450 Å, indicating a lifetime against decomposition of the order of 10^{-13} sec for the excited molecule. If this figure were exact and if the molecule required 2×10^{-12} sec after neutralization to reach the wall, only about one molecule in 10^9 could reach the wall before decomposing.

Even after the polyatomic molecule comes into contact with the surface, i.e., within range of the van der Waals forces, a transfer of electronic excitation energy from the chemical bond in which it was originally localized, across several other bonds to an electron in the metal, is still less likely than a decomposition. The secondary emission is therefore very small.

We must also note that a radiation lifetime of 10^{-7} sec implies that one molecule per 10^6 will radiate instead of decomposing. Since the photoelectric yield for the cathode surfaces used is of the order of 10^{-4} electrons per quantum, the secondary emission from this source amounts to one electron per 10^{10} incident positive ions. We take this figure to represent the total secondary emission. Recombination of secondary electrons with incoming positive ions will further reduce the chance of producing a new avalanche. The average number of ions formed in a selfquenching counter avalanche at the beginning of the Geiger region is about 10^9. Hence the secondary emission is quenched and a single sharp pulse is obtained from a counter filled with methane.

In order to determine whether a given gas by itself will make a selfquenching counter, we have to investigate its absorption spectrum at wave-lengths corresponding to an excitation energy of $I - \phi$. If the absorption spectrum is diffuse or continuous, corresponding to decomposition in this region, then the gas will make a selfquenching counter. To take an example: The ionization energy of ethyl alcohol is 11.3 ev and the neutralized molecule is formed about 1700 Å above the ground state. The spectrum of the vapor shows continuous absorption below 2000 Å, and this is accompanied by photo-decomposition. The quantum yield of the photo-decomposition is of the order of unity. Hence, we should expect alcohol vapor to make a selfquenching counter. A diatomic molecule generally possesses discrete states between the dissociation energy and the ionization energy; thus, on neutralization a diatomic molecule will not decompose. Therefore, counters filled with diatomic gases show non-selfquenching counter action. Since, on the other hand, a heavy organic molecule has a large probability of predissociating at all energies, such a gas will invariably make a selfquenching counter.

The triatomic gases must be considered separately. The absorption spectra of H_2O, CO_2, N_2O, SO_2, H_2S, and CS_2 show bands with diffuse rotational structure converging on the ionization energy of the molecule as a limit. The broadening of the levels would correspond to a lifetime of the order of 100 times that of a heavy molecule. Hence secondary emission would be much more probable. The mentioned triatomic gases (used in conjunction with low resistances) give no evidence of an appreciable Geiger region.

A further consequence of the suppression of secondary emission outlined above, is that the frequency and multiplicity of multiple pulses should increase slowly along the plateau of a selfquenching counter. The numerical estimates of secondary emission given above would lead one to expect about one double pulse in ten or one triple pulse in one hundred at the beginning of the Geiger region. This is roughly in agreement with what one observes on the oscilloscope screen. As the voltage across the counter is raised, the charge collected per count is found to vary linearly with the overvoltage. Measurements [S3] along part of the plateau show that the charge increases by a factor of more than ten. An increase in the number of ions reaching the cathode results in an increased secondary emission and a corresponding increase in the frequency and multiplicity of multiple pulses. From the numerical estimates given above, one would expect that toward the end of the plateau several secondary electrons would on the average be emitted when the positive ion sheath reached the cylinder. In these circumstances practically every pulse would be a multiple of large multiplicity; indeed, the oscilloscope shows sprays of multiple pulses toward the end of the Geiger region. If electronic circuits of high resolving power for fast counting are used with a counter operating in this manner, these multiple pulses will give rise to many spurious counts. The slope of the counting-rate plateau is thus to be attributed to the increasing frequency and multiplicity of the multiple pulses leading to an increasing number of spurious counts. The Geiger region terminates when the secondary emission becomes great enough to make the discharge self-sustaining. The Geiger plateau does not terminate abruptly, but as the voltage is raised more and more multiple pulses are observed.

So far the discussion has been restricted to selfquenching counters containing a pure polyatomic gas. If we consider next a selfquenching counter which contains a mixture of a quenching and a non-quenching gas, the question arises of how the secondary emission is suppressed. Since a counter containing 90% argon to 10% alcohol is selfquenching, it is necessary to explain why no argon ions reach the cathode when there is a small amount of alcohol present. The explanation depends on the relative magnitude of the ionization potentials (see Table 4–4) of the two gases: 11.3 volts for $C_2H_5(OH)$ and 15.7

TABLE 4–4. IONIZATION POTENTIALS OF SUBSTANCES USED AS GASES IN COUNTERS *

Substance	Symbol	Ionization Potential in Volts
Alcohol (ethyl)	$C_2H_5(OH)$	11.3
Ammonia	NH_3	11.2
Argon	A	15.68
Ethane	C_2H_6	12.8
Helium	He	24.46
Hydrogen	H_2	15.6
Iodine (vapor)	I_2	9.7
Mercury	Hg	10.39
Methane	CH_4	14.5
Neon	Ne	21.74
Nitrogen	N_2	15.51
Oxygen	O_2	12.5
Water (vapor)	H_2O	12.56
Xenon	Xe	12.08

* *Handbook of Chemistry and Physics; Int. Crit. Tables.*

volts for argon. Electron transfer takes place during the passage of the ion sheath across the counter. During this time the argon ions make about 10^5 collisions with alcohol molecules. Since the ionization energy of the argon atom is greater than the ionization energy of the alcohol molecule, an electron can be transferred from the molecule to the ion. The reverse process, namely, a transfer of an electron from an argon atom to an alcohol ion is energetically impossible because the kinetic energies are only about 0.1 ev. The transfer is accompanied by the emission of a photon of 4.4 ev (difference of the ionization energies) which is absorbed by the alcohol vapor. This effect has been investigated by Kallmann and Rosen,[K8] who found that the cross section for electron transfer is of the order of magnitude of the gas kinetic cross section in the case of an ion beam moving through a gas of the same species. In the case of an ion beam moving through a gas of a different ionization potential, the cross section is somewhat less, but no appreciable number of argon ions can reach the cathode after 10^5 collisions. In the commonly used selfquenching counters containing a mixture of gases, the ionization potential of the polyatomic constituent is invariably less than that of the inert gas. If the situation could be reversed, so that the inert gas has the lower ionization potential, then electron transfer would take place in the reverse direction and no polyatomic ions would reach the cathode. In such a counter, photons would be quenched but not the secondary emission. Experimental tests bear this out.

3. Operation. *a. Introduction.* Our discussion of the operational characteristics of selfquenching counters will follow that already given for the non-selfquenching type. The same operating desiderata, namely, low operating potential, long operating range, high efficiency, stability with use and time, and large pulse-size, short recovery time and small temperature coefficient, will be reviewed in turn. The several desirable features are to a certain extent mutually exclusive, in the sense that not all can be attained to a maximum degree with any one arrangement. The interdependence will be discussed and we will point out which have to be sacrificed for the others. It will suffice here to say that there is no ideal "formula" for filling or operating counters, and that the filling substances selected will be determined by the use to be made of the counter and so will differ for different problems.

The chief advantage of the selfquenching counter over the non-selfquenching one is described in the name. In the self-quenching type the discharge terminates or is "quenched" due to the internal mechanism which we have described, and hence no electronic quenching circuit or high resistance is necessary. The disadvantage of the high resistance, as has already been pointed out, is that it lengthens the recovery time of the counter. The equivalent vacuum tube circuit permits a short time constant to be used but adds the inconvenience of an extra stage in the electronic circuits. The advantage gained in the elimination of the quenching resistor or circuit is secured at the price of stability, for the act of quenching also decomposes a fraction of the polyatomic gas or vapor in the counter. We shall show how long a useful life may be expected.

b. Starting and operating potentials. The starting and operating potentials of selfquenching counters are in general somewhat higher than those of the non-selfquenching. When a counter is filled with pure argon, and a cm or two of alcohol or any other vapor is added, the starting potential is raised, usually by several hundred volts. Thus the same counter which might operate at 800 volts filled with argon will require perhaps 1100 when the quenching constituent is added. This is a disadvantage only when batteries are used, for a stabilized voltage supply operating on AC (see Chapter 7) and supplying 1500 volts is no more difficult to build than one supplying 1000.

Polyatomic gases in general require higher voltages than do the monatomic ones. For example, a counter filled with pure methane or butane or boron trifluoride will require a higher potential than will the same counter if filled to the same pressure with a mixture consisting of 90% argon and 10% alcohol, ether or amyl acetate vapor. The operating potential increases with the gas pressure, and may reach high values. For example, a counter 15 cm in diameter and filled to 50 cm pressure with BF_3 will require about 5000 volts if neutrons are to be detected and a pulse of 10^{-2} volt amplitude is required. Typical curves are shown in Fig. 4–9 for several cases, in which

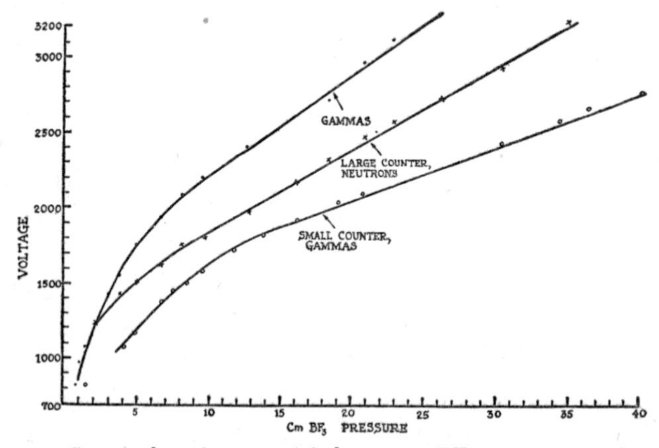

Fig. 4–9. Curves of starting potentials for neutron BF_3 counters, counting neutrons and gamma rays. Note that the voltage difference between the neutron and beta detection potentials increases with the BF_3 pressure. Large counter 5.5 cm diameter, 22.7 cm long. Small counter 1 cm diameter, 3 cm long, central wire 3 mil. Pulse size, constant, about 0.1 volt. (From S. A. Korff, *Rev. Mod. Phys.* 14, 1–11 (1942))

the starting potentials for a large and a small counter, filled with BF_3, are plotted against pressure. The counters may be used to detect neutrons or gamma rays. The large counter will require higher operating voltages than the small counter and will detect gammas at a higher voltage than is required to detect neutrons because the neutron pulse is larger.

Since argon has a considerably lower starting potential than BF_3, the addition of about ten percent of argon to a counter containing pure BF_3 will lower the starting potential somewhat. The total gas pressure will be increased accordingly.

The efficiency for detecting neutrons is determined by the amount of BF_3 and hence is not altered by adding argon.

c. Flatness of the plateau. The flatness of the plateau is determined by the nature of the quenching constituent. If pure argon and pure (absolute) alcohol are used, flat plateaus may be secured. A series of tests was conducted by Spatz [S1] in which he found that (1) the flatness of the plateau was materially reduced by contaminating an alcohol-argon mixture with air, and (2) the flatness depended on the amount of alcohol. The flatness of the plateau is defined as the percentage increase in counting rate as the voltage is raised. He found that the plateau could be made absolutely flat to within the experimental error, i.e., a rise in counting rate of less than 1% for a 100 volt increase in operating voltage, if a 95% argon, 5% alcohol mixture were used, and the argon was 99.8% pure and the alcohol absolute. Admitting as much as 2% air caused the plateau slope to increase to a 15% rise per 100 volts. Filling the same counter to a total of 80% argon and 20% alcohol yielded a slope of 5% per 100 volts. He attributed the increase of slope with alcohol content to air dissolved in the alcohol. Similar unpublished tests on other polyatomic vapors yield essentially the same result. As has previously been pointed out, the departure from flatness of the plateau is a measure of the number of spurious counts. The addition of air, resulting in occasional negative ion formation, causes spurious counts.

d. Efficiency. The factors governing the efficiency of counters have already been discussed. Eq. (4–3) may be used in computing the values to be expected. In a counter containing a mixture of gases the number of ion-pairs formed will depend on the specific ionization of each of the constituents and on the pressure of each. A counter 2 cm in diameter to 10 cm with argon will have an efficiency of 99.7% and the addition of 1 or 2 cm of alcohol or ether will raise the efficiency to perhaps 99.8%. The specific ionization of many organic vapors has not been measured but it may be assumed to be fairly high because of the large number of electrons per molecule. However, the argon constituent will dominate in the case cited. A counter filled with alcohol vapor alone would have a much lower efficiency, since the vapor pressure of ethyl alcohol is only 4.4 cm at 20° C and hence there would be an insufficient total amount of gas in the counter. Further, such a counter would have a marked temperature coefficient (see below). Filling a counter with quenching gas alone can be done successfully with such gases as BF_3, or methane or butane which can be introduced to a total pressure of from 8 to 15 cm or more without liquefying at normal operating temperatures. The specific ionization of these gases is such that good efficiencies may be obtained with filling pressures comparable to those used in argon-alcohol or argon-ether or argon-amyl acetate counters.

e. Stability. As has been pointed out before, selfquenching counters all suffer from the disadvantage that the quenching constituent is decomposed in the act of quenching and hence the characteristics of the counters vary with use. Time, by itself, appears to have no effect, and counters which have been carefully prepared but not used have been found, after a lapse of several years, to be as good as new ones. A series of tests of expected "lives" of counters has been made by Spatz.[S1] The word "life" is taken to mean the number of counts which the counter can detect before it changes so much as to become useless.

The number of molecules decomposed in each discharge will depend on the overvoltage. Operating counters at high overvoltages will therefore decrease the life, and causing a counter to "flash over" or go into a continuous discharge by applying voltages in excess of the operating potential near the top of the plateau may indeed ruin a counter in quite a short time. In the average case, however, about 10^{10} molecules are decomposed in each discharge. This corresponds to the production, according to eq. (1–1) of about a 100 volt pulse on a wire system, having a 16 micromicrofarad distributed capacity. Since a counter contains roughly 10^{20} molecules of alcohol, we should expect a life of the order of 10^{10} counts, which is in good agreement with Spatz's findings for argon-alcohol mixtures. For methane he finds somewhat lower values, nearer 10^8 counts, which is presumably due to the fact that a methane molecule decomposes directly into a non-quenching gas, hydrogen, whereas more complex molecules may decompose first into other constituents which are still polyatomic and so may be able to "quench" even after they have taken part in several discharges. A long lifetime will hence be gained by (a) using a heavy, complex molecule, (b) having as much of it as possible in the counter, and (c) operating always at low overvoltages. These features, if incorporated, will usually entail some sacrifice of flatness of plateau, a high operating voltage, and a longer recovery time.

As the quenching constituent is decomposed, the total number of molecules in the counter increases. We should expect therefore that the pressure in a counter would increase with use. This is found to be the case. Spatz reports changes of pressure in both argon-alcohol and methane counters. Concomitant with such changes in pressure, there is to be expected an increase in starting potential, since this depends on pressure. This also is observed. The starting potential may change by 100 volts or more during the life of an argon-alcohol counter. Further, the plateau is also observed to become less flat with use, and a counter with a plateau initially flat to within experimental error will show an appreciable slope after a certain amount of use.

Consequently, as the counter is used, the following changes take place: (a) the operating potential increases, (b) the pressure increases, (c) the plateau becomes less flat. These changes in characteristics can usually be allowed for and will not interfere with accurate measurements providing they are recognized. The life of 10^{10} counts will serve for most experiments.

Eventually, however, a selfquenching counter will have to be pumped and refilled. A non-selfquenching counter is better, in that its operating characteristics are more stable with use and its life is determined not by decomposition of the gas but by pitting of the central wire under repeated discharges. A longer life will generally be secured for non-selfquenching counters.

f. Recovery time. The natural insensitive time of a counter is determined by the migration time of the positive ions. This we have already discussed, and we have cited the measured times for selfquenching counters as of the order of 10^{-4} sec. Thus Simpson finds between 1.0 and 2.9×10^{-4} sec for argon-alcohol counters, while for the heavier amyl acetate molecule in the same counter, 6 to 8×10^{-4} second. Similarly, a non-selfquenching counter, employing argon, might be expected to have a shorter recovery time because the mobility of the argon ions is greater than that of the organic ones. This is also found to be the case, and thus the commonly used designation of "fast" counter for the selfquenching type is exactly the reverse of a true description. Here again the interdependence of the desirable characteristics of counters is to be noted, since the heavy molecules which will give the longest useful counter lives also give the counter a longer resolving time. For fast counting problems therefore, light molecules should be used, or non-selfquenching counters employed, while for long-period observations at not too high counting rates, fillings using heavier molecules will be advantageous.

g. Temperature coefficient. Various observers [K9] have commented that the counting rate of selfquenching counters exhibits a temperature dependence which can at times be troublesome. This effect has been explained as due to the fact that most of the heavy organic compounds are vapors at room temperature, and therefore a decrease in temperature of any substantial amount may cause some of the quenching constituent to condense out. Two results follow: (a) there may be insufficient quenching material left to completely quench the discharge and (b) the liquid may condense near the electrodes in such a way as to cause semi-conducting paths across the insulating material between the wire and cylinder. Leakage across such paths can manifest itself as spurious counts. Hence care should be taken in filling counters not to introduce organic vapor to such an amount that any will condense at the lowest temperature at which the counter is to be used. Other observers [C5] report that non-selfquenching counters show negligible temperature coefficients. This is also to be expected, providing that the counters are so constructed that the inner surfaces are chemically stable and do not evolve gas if the counter experiences moderate temperature changes. Thus, for example, the use of hard rubber plugs for the ends of counters, or inadequate cleaning, may give rise to temperature effects. Temperature coefficients are largely produced by variations in the total number (and kind) of atoms or molecules; while if the total number is not varied and the pressure rises because of increase in temperature, little trouble is experienced.

h. Operating resistance. The choice of the operating resistance of a selfquenching counter is important. Referring to Fig. 1–1, it will be seen that a resistance R is necessary, in order to permit coupling the counter to the vacuum tube circuit which follows. It is the voltage pulse, developed across this resistance, which is detected. In the case of the resistance-quenched counters it is this resistance which produces the long time constant referred to above. For selfquenching counters, no resistance is needed to quench the discharge, but one is required in order to produce a voltage swing for transmission to the grid of the tube and also to permit the counter wire to recover rapidly to its initial voltage so that it will be sensitive for the next pulse. If the resistance is made too high, the recovery time constant will be too long. If the resistance is too low, the voltage swing of the grid will be small.

Let us assume that the counter wire is connected directly

to the grid of an ordinary vacuum tube. The distributed capacity of the counter wire, tube grid and leads may then be of the order of 10 micromicrofarads, or higher if the counter is far removed from the grid, and long connecting cables are used. If the resistance R is chosen of 1 megohm, the RC time constant will be 10^{-5} sec. This is shorter than the natural insensitive time of the counter, and hence little is gained by making the resistance lower. An additional factor of ten is sometimes used, if extremely short revolving times (10^{-6} sec) are required and the counter is operated on the "break" of the discharge. In this case a resistance of the order of 10^5 ohms is used and sensitive circuits are required as the pulse is small. In general 10^5 ohms can represent a useful lower limit. On the upper side, a resistance of more than 10 megohms will introduce appreciable time delay into the recovery. Hence a resistance of between 0.1 and 2 megohms is the best for most cases.

If the resistance is lowered below 0.1 megohm, the pulse received on the grid of the vacuum tube becomes small. Further, the resistor serves as a protective device. A megohm will limit to a milliampere the current that can flow if (at 1000 volts) the counter should be accidentally operated above the Geiger plateau and go into a continuous discharge, or if the operator should inadvertently come into contact with portions of the device.

i. Effects of mercury vapor. Many investigators have speculated regarding the effect of small amounts of mercury vapor on the operation of a counter. It will be recalled that the vapor pressure of mercury at room temperature is about 10^{-3} mm, and since precautions to exclude it entirely are usually not taken, it may be assumed that it is present to this amount in many counters. In a series of tests, Korff and Present [K7] sought to ascertain what effects might be ascribed to it.

First it should be pointed out that mercury vapor is monatomic and hence a non-selfquenching gas. Second, in amount it is roughly 10^{-5} of other gases. Hence we might expect that it would have roughly the same effect as a like amount of some other non-quenching gas present as an impurity. Such effects are so small as to be undetectable. An occasional mercury atom becomes ionized, and the positive mercury ion will progress to the cylinder and be neutralized along with the other positives. The percentage present is not enough to affect the starting or operating voltages.

A possible effect may be expected because of the magnitude of the ionization potential, 10.4 volts. This is less than that of some organic molecules (see Table 4–4) and hence we might expect that electron transfer would occur and that positive mercury ions would reach the cylinder. In being neutralized these might be expected to emit recombination radiation and hence provide a source of secondary (photo) electrons. However, since the amount present is so small, say one part in 10^5, and since the average ion on its way out to the cylinder only makes between 10^4 and 10^5 collisions, the number of mercury ions which are produced either in the avalanche or by transfer is small. Now since the photoelectric efficiency is low, about 10^{-4}, then 10^4 mercury ions would have to become neutralized at the cathode in order to produce even one secondary electron. Therefore we might expect, as experiment bears out, that no significant effects are to be observed at room temperature.

If, however, the mercury vapor pressure were increased by a factor of 100 or so, enough mercury ions would be neutralized at the cylinder to produce observable effects. This was accomplished in the experiments cited by introducing a small drop of mercury into the counter and then heating the counter to about 82° C, at which temperature the vapor pressure is 0.1 mm. When mercury is present at these pressures, the behavior of a normal selfquenching counter becomes erratic.

Occasional enormous pulses are observed and at slightly higher pressures the counter tends to go into a quasi-continuous discharge.

Thus it is a matter of good fortune that the pressure of mercury vapor at room temperature is sufficiently low so that mercury produces negligible effects. For this reason, no especial pains need be taken to exclude it from the counters, and in the discussions we shall disregard its presence.

CHAPTER 5

PREPARATION AND CONSTRUCTION OF COUNTERS

A. General Considerations in Construction

1. Construction. In constructing a counter to be used in the detection of any type of radiation, electromagnetic or corpuscular, it is desirable to attempt to approximate as closely as possible several desiderata. First, the counter must be designed with regard to the nature and distribution of the radiation being studied. This includes providing means whereby radiation with small penetrating power, such as alpha particles, can reach the sensitive part of the counter. Second, the counter should have as low a natural background as possible, and undesired radiation should be excluded. Third, the counter should not have spurious counts, for these will vitiate interpretations based on a statistical analysis of the data since their probability of occurrence is not random, and will introduce a variable background which it is difficult to allow for accurately. To these features may also be added simplicity of construction, ruggedness, forms convenient for use, and low cost.

The methods that will be described, for the preparation and construction of counters, have been developed as a result of the application of two fundamental principles. The first is that the construction and preparation should be such as to permit the mechanism of the counter discharge to operate, with a minimum of disturbing effects due to unwanted agencies. The second principle is that the procedures should insure that the desired conditions remain as permanently as possible. An illustration of the application of the first of these principles is the following: The cylinder of the counter should be made of substances with high work functions and alkali metals should be especially avoided. This is important because the supply of secondary electrons, which causes the discharge to continue, and thus tends to defeat the processes quenching the discharge, is dependent on the work function. The number of secondary electrons can be greatly reduced by proper choice of cathode surface, and the counter will accordingly have better operating characteristics. An illustration of the second principle, to insure permanence, is in the desirability of cleaning the counter thoroughly before filling and sealing it. If, for example, the counter contains adsorbed films of material which, over a period of time, will change, then the chemical composition of the gas in the counter will alter with time and the properties of the counter will change accordingly.

In the past, many persons have claimed that some of the precautions suggested below were unnecessary. While it may be possible in individual cases to disregard certain ones and still occasionally to produce a good counter, yet the reason for each of the procedures appears sufficiently cogent to warrant its use. Over a period of some years during which some thousands of counters have been constructed, it has been found possible to make counters in lots of 100 at a time and to have all but one or two be acceptable, in the sense of having long, flat plateaus and low backgrounds. Other counters have been kept for years before use; and had they not been chemically stable they would almost certainly not have remained constantly usable. Several are still serviceable which were made nine years ago. The problem is similar to that of the construction of radio tubes. While it may be possible to get an occasional good tube if the thorough cleaning and evacuation techniques are neglected the production of many with reproducible and predictable characteristics is greatly facilitated by attention to these details.

B. Constructional Features

Counters can be constructed with an astonishingly wide variety of characteristics and physical dimensions. To illustrate the possible ranges in size, counters 4 mm in radius and 9 mm long may be contrasted with others 75 mm in radius and 1 meter in length. Both these sizes are in successful operation at the present time and there appears to be no reason why these dimensions cannot be considerably exceeded in either direction should it prove desirable to do so. The nature of the problem to be studied largely determines the size and shape of the counters used. For example, if a large sensitive area is required, as often occurs in cosmic ray investigations, it is usual to arrange a layer or tray of long narrow counters and to connect the wires either together or in coincidence (see Chapter 7). A single counter of great size would perform this same function but would also have a considerable sensitive volume not used directly in the experiment and hence would contribute unnecessarily to the background. In addition, a single big counter would require a higher operating potential. On the other hand, for detecting a small number of neutrons, such as the number produced by the cosmic radiation at sea level, a large sensitive volume is desired and a single counter of maximum dimensions is indicated. Still another problem is the detection of weak beta radiation from small samples, a common phenomenon in tracer research in medicine or biophysics. Here a small counter with low background but with a maximum efficiency in terms of sensitive solid angle is necessary. We shall describe such counters in the paragraphs on thin windows.

The geometry of most counters is cylindrical. The optimum length and diameter of the cylinder will be determined by the problem. There are no fundamental limitations on either, except that a cylinder whose radius is larger than its length will have a field distribution which varies along its axis, so that different parts of the counter will be operating at different effective potentials. Further, spherical geometry can be used if desirable. A small round bead on the end of a wire projecting into the center of a sphere will serve as a collecting electrode and the shell as the spherical cathode.

A desirable feature which should be included whenever possible is that both ends of the central wire should be electrically available from the outside of the counter. This is important in that it will enable the wire to be glowed while the counter is evacuated. This operation will effectively remove microscopic bits of dust or lint or metal or sharp points on the wire. If left, these would create local irregularities in the electric field, which in turn may cause local ionization and hence spurious counts. Further, glowing the wire drives off occluded gases and hence contributes to chemical stability.

The wire diameter is one factor determining the operating voltage. It is desirable, in order to secure low voltages, to have this diameter as small as possible. Ordinarily, 3 or 4 mil tungsten wire is used, for larger diameter wire causes the required voltages to increase unnecessarily, while smaller diameter wire is so fragile that the wire is too readily broken in ordinary handling. Tungsten is a good material for the wires because (a) it can readily be sealed to glass and (b) it can be heated successfully while the counter is being pumped.

Sharp points in the high field regions must be avoided as these give rise to local ionization and spurious counts. The ends of the cylinder should be slightly rounded outward, to decrease the field gradually, and the inside of the cylinder should be free from burrs, scratches or irregularities. Similarly the wire should be smooth. The places where the wire is welded onto the supports should be shielded, preferably with glass sleeves, so that high local fields are avoided. Such sleeves are shown in Fig. 5–1A and elsewhere.

Copper is a good material for the counter cylinder. Brass may also be used and is frequently available in suitable shapes.

If anything, it is a little less good than copper, due to the increased photosensitivity of the zinc content. Any trace of the alkali metals must be scrupulously avoided. Aluminum is undesirable for two reasons. It is often porous and hard to outgas. Further, with certain filling gases, electrons may be liberated from its surface by chemical action, and thus it may produce spurious counts. Soft solder on parts of a counter is undesirable as the counter can then not be heated enough to outgas thoroughly. In certain types of construction, this is hard to avoid, but it should be regarded as a definite disadvantage. Soft solder is also attacked by cleaning solutions.

Light should be kept from reaching the interior of the counter. This is especially important if the ultraviolet content of the light is high. This can be accomplished in many ways. The counter may be operated inside a suitable shield. Black paper is opaque to light yet does not affect any but the softest beta rays. The glass surfaces of the counter may be coated with an opaque wax (see below), or the shape of the envelope may exclude virtually all ambient illumination. The purpose of excluding light is to reduce the number of photoelectrons and spurious counts.

Waxed joints of any kind should also be avoided. These can seldom be made permanently tight. They are attacked by cleaning fluids, and prevent the counter's being heated to outgas it. Moreover, they are often attacked by the organic filling materials and hence are chemically unstable. Further, they may evolve gas and render the counting-rate temperature dependent.

C. Envelopes

Counters can be made with either glass or metal envelopes. In the metal envelope type, the tube itself is usually also the cathode of the counter. For safety in handling, it is customary to operate such counters with the cylinder at ground potential. The appropriate circuits are given in Chapter 7. Glass containers, on the other hand, permit either cylinder or wire to be operated at ground potential. Glass counters are also somewhat better adapted to the cleaning techniques which we shall describe in the following section. Most metal envelope designs

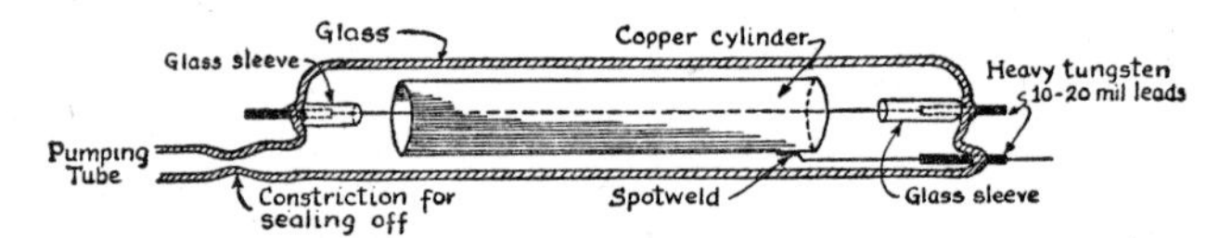

Fig. 5–1A. Glass envelope counter.

involve soldered joints which would be attacked by the cleaning acids.

Several designs which have been used successfully are shown in Figs. 5–1A and B, those indicated by A being in glass envelopes while those marked B employ a metal cathode as the outside element. The cylinder can be quite thin in the case of the glass envelope types. Seamless copper tubing of 0.2 mm thickness will serve admirably. When the cylinder also serves as the wall of the counter, it must of course be rugged enough to

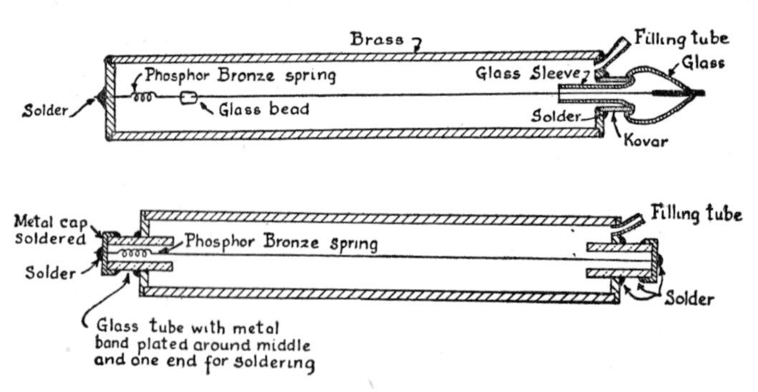

Fig. 5–1B. Metal envelope counters.

withstand atmospheric pressure and also the shocks of ordinary handling. Consequently thicker stock is required, 0.5 mm brass often being used. Thus the metal exterior counters require more metal; but they require less glass blowing and are somewhat easier to mass-produce if a good glass blower is not available. The glass counters can usually be cleaned more thoroughly.

In the early days of counters, it was often the custom to employ a brass tube as a cathode and to wax hard rubber stoppers into the ends. Such construction should be avoided because (a) it is virtually impossible to clean, (b) the parts give off gas and change the counter characteristics with time, and (c) in the case of BF_3 counters, the gas attacks the ends and the counter soon becomes useless.

In making glass envelope counters for neutron measurements, the neutron absorption due to the boron content of glass must be considered. Thus for measurements in which very low neutron intensities are expected, the types of glass such as Pyrex having high boron content should be avoided. If it is necessary to use such glass, the absorption of neutrons in the glass should be computed and allowed for [see eq. (6–8)].

D. Thin Window and Large Solid Angle Counters

The problem of getting the particle to be detected into the counter is especially important with (a) weak sources and (b) the types of radiation which have small penetrating power. Two procedures are in general available, first to place the source of radiation inside the counter, and second to employ a thin window on the counter through which the radiation may be projected into the sensitive volume. To illustrate the thinness required of the window, we recall that most alpha particles have a range of only 4 or 5 cm of air. The window must consequently not be thicker than a few centimeters of air-equivalent, or say some 0.05 mm or less of glass.

Extremely thin glass bubbles can be blown on the ends of glass tubing, and hence an arrangement such as is shown in Fig. 5–2A is readily constructed. If the source of alpha or other radiation of low penetrating power is put next to this window, the particles will have the maximum opportunity of entering the counter. The source cannot be moved many centimeters in air from the window because of the short range in air of the radiation. Placing counter and source in an evacuated container is possible but is inconvenient, and further a

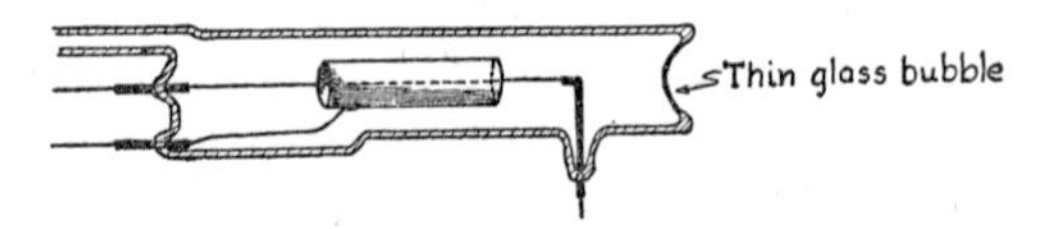

Fig. 5–2A. Counter with thin end window for alpha particles.

thin window will be able to withstand quite a pressure differential only if the glass is always under tension. The counter should thus have less pressure on the inside than outside.

Re-entrant thin glass windows as in Fig. 5–2B may be used, through which alpha particles can be projected into proportional counters for calibrating purposes. If the thickness of the window is known, the amount of ionization produced by the particle in the counter can be readily estimated. If the

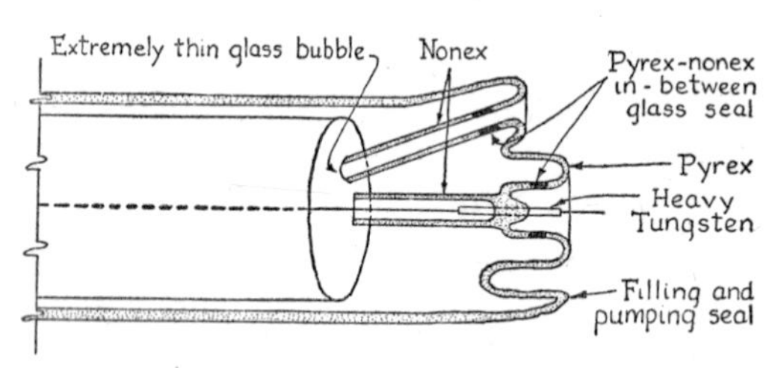

Fig. 5–2B. Construction of thin window on counter to permit alpha particles for calibration to be projected into the sensitive volume with minimum loss of range. An extremely thin glass bubble is attached to the end of a tube entering the volume of the counter, and a rod with some mesothorium or polonium on one end is lowered through the tube and brought near the window. (Ref. K4)

source is now withdrawn one cm in air from the window, the amount of ionization produced in the counter is less by the amount produced in the 1 cm of air. In this manner a curve can be obtained of the pulse size as a function of the amount of ionization liberated in the counter. The thickness of the window can be determined by raising the voltage on the counter until it is operating in the Geiger region. The source is now withdrawn until the counter just ceases to count the particles

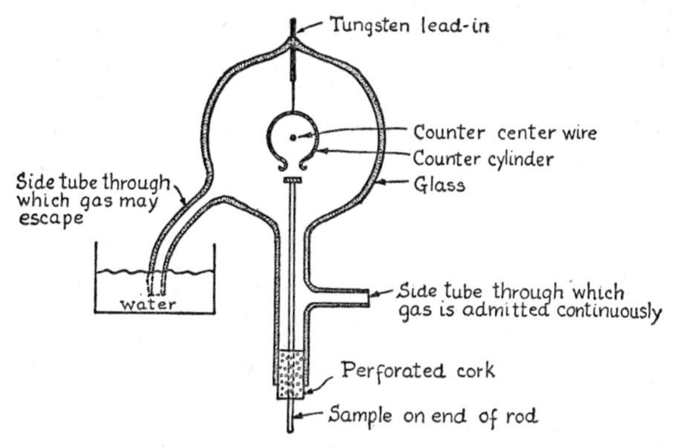

Fig. 5–2C. Counter arranged to contain gas at atmospheric pressure so that samples may be readily brought near sensitive volume with no intervening windows. Helium or argon at atmospheric pressure will produce counters with reasonable starting potentials. (After S. C. Brown, B3)

which the source emits. If we designate by D the distance of the source from the window at which counts are just detected, and by W the window thickness in air-equivalent, then the range R of the particles is evidently equal to $D + W$. Since R is known for the various alpha radiations and D has just been measured, W is determined. This term also includes the

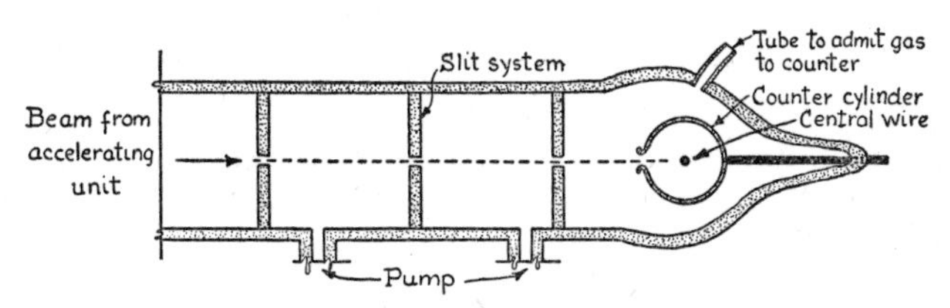

Fig. 5–2D. Counter attached directly to accelerating apparatus.

thickness in air-equivalent of the gas inside the counter which the particle must penetrate to reach the sensitive region. The particle need produce only one ion, once it has reached the sensitive region, in order to record a count if the counter is operating in the Geiger region. The end of the range is thus readily found.

Another arrangement for weak sources is shown in Fig. 5–2C. Counters of this type have been used by Brown [B4] and others. In this case, the source is raised directly into the sensitive volume. A stream of helium is flowed continuously through the counter, and the gas in the counter is at full atmospheric pressure. No sealing-off provisions are necessary in this case. No window exists and ionization is produced along the entire path of the particles in the gas of the counter.

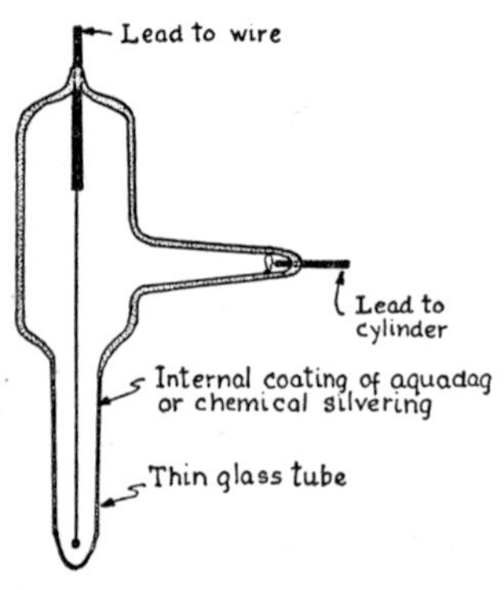

FIG. 5–3A. Thin-walled counter suitable for immersion in liquids containing minute radioactive traces.

In other cases it is possible to attach the counter directly to the accelerating apparatus, and to project the particles to be studied into the counter directly. A typical arrangement of this sort is shown in Fig. 5–2D, where the beam passes through narrow slits into the counter. The pressure in the counter can be kept high enough for counting action by admitting gas through an adjustable leak, while pumping between the slits will keep the gas out of the accelerating chamber. If the particles in the beam have any appreciable penetrating power, thin windows may be placed over the slits and the slits considerably increased in size. The windows in this case need only withstand the difference in pressure between the counter and the accelerating tube, perhaps a total of 0.1 to 0.2 atm.

For the detection of weak beta radiation, a problem which arises both in medicine in radioactive tracer research and in certain problems of nuclear physics, another design is often used. Not only has the beta radiation often low penetrating power, but it is frequently so small in absolute amount as to render its detection above the normal statistical background difficult. It is therefore important that as large a fraction as possible of the beta radiation emitted by the source should reach the sensitive portion of the counter. This in turn means

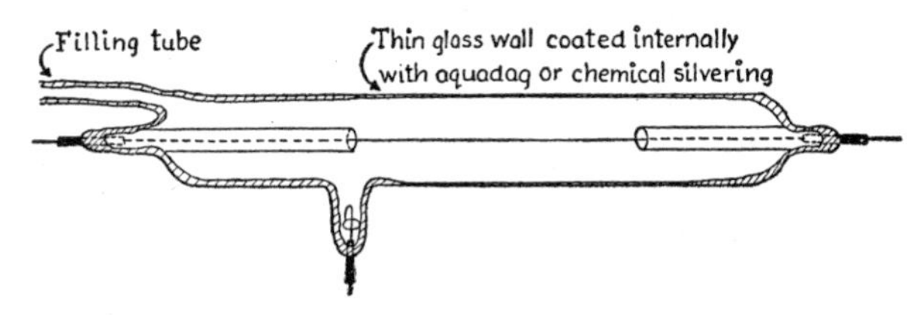

FIG. 5–3B. Thin-walled beta ray counter.

that the radiation in all directions from the source should be available to the counter, or in other words that the counter should have a large sensitive solid angle.

Radiation from a solution may be measured either by lowering a thin-walled counter such as shown in Fig. 5–3A into the solution or by placing a thin-walled counter directly above it.

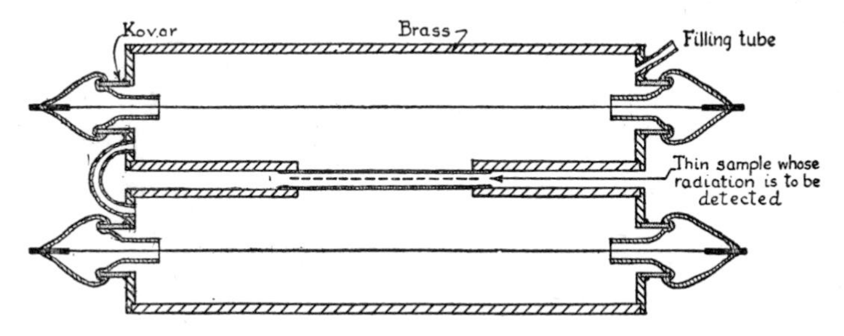

FIG. 5–3C. Double counter for measuring radiation from both sides of thin sample.

A beta-counter suitable for this purpose is shown in Fig. 5–3B. Virtually all the radiation from one side of a thin foil may be measured with counters of this type by curling the foil to the same diameter as the thin portion of the counter and laying it on the thin part.

For coverage of still greater solid angles, such as for detecting radiation from both sides of a foil, Simpson [S5] has devised an arrangement of two counters as shown in Fig. 5–3C. Here each counter has a section covered by a thin window which can be made of any suitable substance such as cellophane or nickel silver foil, and the two thin sections are placed together. The wires of the counters may then be connected together and the discharges of both recorded. If the opening in the counters is to be large and the window thin, it may be necessary to provide some support behind the window to prevent the window from collapsing under atmospheric pressure. This can readily be arranged by placing a wire mesh or narrow reinforcing strips behind the window. These reinforcements will somewhat reduce the sensitive aperture but can generally be made narrow enough not to obscure too large a fraction of the area.

2. Evacuation and Filling. *a. Washing and cleaning.* It has been repeatedly emphasized by Locher [L2] and others that it is important to remove dirt, dust and contamination from the inside of counters. Dust and particles will tend to become electrified in the strong fields, will distort the field and give rise to spurious counts. Contamination may give off gas which will alter the operating characteristics of a counter over a period of time. It is important therefore adequately to wash and clean the inside of the counter. In the glass envelope types, this can readily be accomplished by washing the inside of the counter with a dilute mixture of sulphuric and nitric acids, allowing the solution to stay in the counter until it has vigorously attacked the cathode and removed all surface contamination, and then cleaning out all the acid with distilled water. In the metal envelope types, the ends are usually attached with solder and the acid treatment cannot therefore be used. In this case, washing with ammonia and organic solvents will remove most of the impurities and, while not as thorough as the acid, will have to serve. For special counter shapes or designs, special techniques should be devised, but the purpose should always be to remove dust, wax, grease or other extraneous matter.

The chemical stability of the cylinder may be insured by suitable treatment. The cylinder may be either oxidized, by admitting oxygen and heating, or reduced, by heating with hydrogen. Ordinarily, hydrogen should not be used as a filling gas in a counter with an oxidized cylinder, for a chemical reaction will take place which will slowly alter the constituents, and therefore the operating characteristics of the counter.

In making the thin-walled glass counters such as shown in Fig. 5–3B, in which the cathode is chemically silvered or coated with colloidal carbon (Aquadag), the glass must be thoroughly cleaned before the cathode surface is applied, so that the painted surface will adhere firmly. Both chemical silvering and graphite have a tendency to peel off in flakes if the surface is not clean, and these flakes are immediately so oriented in the field that they form sharp points and hence may give rise to spurious counts. Baking to outgas counters of this type is not practicable as it tends to destroy the cathode surface; but the central wire can be glowed in the design shown in Fig. 5–3B.

b. Evacuation. The thoroughly cleaned counters may next be sealed onto a vacuum system and evacuated. It is desirable to obtain a good vacuum. Prolonged pumping with diffusion pumps is recommended. The counters should be heated if feasible, to drive off gases occluded on the surfaces. This procedure is of course to be carried out with caution if the counter has soldered joints or is internally silvered, but glass-envelope types can be given extensive heat treatment. If a group of counters is to be filled, they may all be mounted on a manifold and the entire arrangement placed in an electric furnace. Baking under vacuum follows the customary techniques for obtaining high vacua. It is not necessary to take elaborate precautions to eliminate mercury vapor, for experiments have shown [K7] that the amount present at room temperature is of no consequence.

The wire should be glowed. This can readily be accomplished by connecting the ends of the wire to a Variac, and slowly raising the voltage. Usually a few volts is enough to produce incandescence. The importance of this procedure has been emphasized by Locher, who points out that it not only burns off dust and sharp points on the wire but also alters the crystalline structure to give greater uniformity and reduces die-scratches on the wire. To enable the wire to be glowed it is necessary that both ends be available electrically. While this cannot always be achieved, as for example in the counter shown in Fig. 5–3A, the importance of glowing the wire is such that serious consideration should be given in the design to arranging for the possibility.

After a good vacuum has been secured, the counter may be filled. The gas chosen will depend on considerations which we have already discussed. Usually it is convenient to store the gases to be used in glass bulbs connected to the counter filling system by stopcocks. The glass bulbs can be thoroughly evacuated and the gases purified if desirable. Stopcocks permit easier and more accurate control of the flow of gas than do the valves on the commercial steel cylinders of gas. A diagram of a suitable system is shown in Fig. 5–4. Mercury manometers should be provided to enable pressures to be measured. Whenever an organic vapor is used, care should be taken that no air is admitted at the same time. The stopcocks should be watched, for many organic liquids suitable for quenching counters also dissolve stopcock grease. Similarly, BF_3 attacks stopcock grease slowly, and occasionally stopcocks should be cleaned and regreased. Enough time for diffusion of heavy vapors should be allowed. In preparing vapor-filled counters the vapor should be admitted first, and then the inert constituent. At least an hour should be allowed for diffusion equilibrium to be established after the mixture is made. The counters should in general be tested while still attached to the system, so that errors in filling can be rectified or operating conditions altered by admitting or removing gas. An oscilloscope and an adjustable voltage supply, as well as a small sample of radioactive material, are all that is necessary for such testing. After filling and testing, the counter is sealed off, and the system pumped to remove the organic vapors,

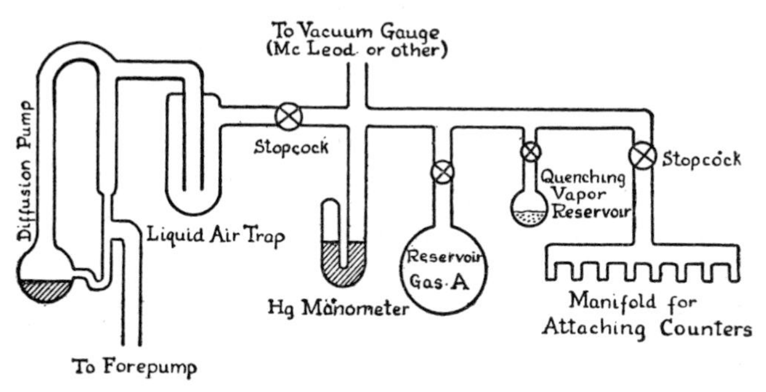

FIG. 5–4. Vacuum system for filling counters.

since these are inflammable, and constitute an explosion hazard if left.

c. External treatment. After a counter has been filled and removed from the system, it is well to wax the glass surfaces. The purpose of this is twofold. The photo-sensitivity of the counter is reduced if an opaque film of wax covers those parts through which light can reach the interior. Various black or dark red fat-soluble dyes (e.g., Sudan IV and others) can be added to the wax to increase its opacity. The second important feature is that this procedure gives the glass surfaces a high resistance, and reduces the formation of surface films of moisture and surface leakage. Since high fields and potentials are used, it is important to eliminate leakage. A very minute amount of charge, leaking across an imperceptible moisture film on a glass surface, or even merely redistributing itself on the surface, can cause spurious counts. A high resistance moisture proof wax, such as Ceresin, is therefore indicated.

3. Summary. We may summarize the recommended techniques thus: Avoid procedures which will (a) leave sharp points of any kind in the volume of the counter, or (b) cause chemical or mechanical or electrical changes with time. The first category includes avoidance of dust or microscopic fibres in the counter, or scratches or burrs on the cylinder or welds on inside connecting leads or pits or die-scratches on the wire. Glowing the wire is helpful. The second group of causes of trouble may be minimized by care in preparation, chemical cleanliness, proper choice of materials, good vacuum technique and construction avoiding features such as organic materials which give off or absorb gas over long periods of time. The desirability of any new features in the construction of counters may often be determined by seeing to what extent the proposed features conform to the two principles mentioned.

Summary of Operational Experience

We may summarize experience with counters by citing some "rules" which, while by no means complete or infallible instructions, seem to the author to embody the most important factors in the successful construction and operation of counters.

In order to secure maximum operational effectiveness the following items should be observed:

1. A counter should never be operated above its rated voltage. To do so may damage or ruin it.

2. A counter should not be permitted to go into a "continuous discharge." If it does, the high potential should be immediately disconnected and not connected again until the voltage has been reduced.

3. The counter should be disconnected from the high potential supply, or the high voltage should be shut off when not in use.

4. The voltages in the various circuits, and the high voltage, should be stabilized and free from major fluctuations.

In construction, the following features should be considered:

1. Avoid dust inside the counter.
2. Avoid any sharp points on the inside, i.e., on the wire or cylinder.
3. Use pure (99%) gases and good vacuum technique, and particularly avoid contamination with air.
4. Avoid getting anything into the counter which will change with time, or which will give off gas or produce chemical reactions.
5. Avoid photosensitive surfaces (except in photo-counters).
6. Arrange or treat exterior surface to minimize electrical leakage.

CHAPTER 6

ERRORS AND CORRECTIONS IN COUNTING

A. Introduction

In the operation of counters, there are several possible sources of inefficiency which, if not recognized and taken into account, may lead to error in the interpretation of the results. First there is the efficiency of the counter itself to be considered. This we shall define as the probability that, when the ionizing event to be studied actually occurs, the counter discharges. The counter may fail to discharge for several possible reasons. The event to be detected may not produce an ion in the sensitive volume. Then the sensitivity of various portions of the counter's volume may be different. Finally, the event may occur before the counter has recovered from the previous count. Quite exact numerical estimates of accuracy are possible for each of these contingencies.

The second type of inefficiency is that encountered if the particle to be counted does not reach the sensitive volume, i.e., is absorbed in the wall of the counter. Third we shall discuss the case of coincidence counting and the efficiencies to be expected in this case and, fourth, the efficiency of proportional counters.

1. Probability that Ionization Will Take Place in the Sensitive Volume. The probability that an ionizing event will occur in the sensitive volume of a counter has been discussed in a preliminary manner under the heading of "efficiency" in Chapter 4. Specifically, the discussion presupposes that if one electron is formed in the sensitive volume, a count will be recorded. This is an extremely severe condition, and the failure to realize it in practice will lead to the production of spurious counts and unreliable data. We repeat, *it actually takes only one electron* to produce a count. If a single electron is produced anywhere within the sensitive volume by any agency other than the event to be studied, a spurious count will be produced.

The counter is assumed to be operating in the Geiger region. If a particle is to be counted, then the particle must produce one ion-pair in the sensitive volume. This may occur due to an ionizing collision, or due to an electron knocked out of the wall of the counter. In most cases the ionization is produced in the gas of the counter. If a non-ionizing photon or neutron is to be detected, this entity must produce a photoelectron in the gas or from the walls, the latter being the more usual, or a Compton electron or nuclear disintegration or a nuclear recoil due to a collision with a nucleus in the wall or gas. If the ionization is produced in the wall, the electron or nuclear particle must get out of the wall and into the gas of the counter. Wall recoils are therefore limited by the range of the recoiling particle in the material of the wall, a phenomenon which was discussed in the section on neutron counters, Chapter 3. The probability of a disintegration occurring is also discussed there.

If a counter is to count photons, a large surface, photosensitive to the radiation to be studied, is desirable. In addition, a window to admit the radiation must be provided. Since the photoelectric efficiency of most surfaces is low, many photons will strike the cathode for one photoelectron ejected. Alkali metals are commonly used for photoelectric surfaces. On the other hand, when particles are to be counted, photon counts are usually unwanted and therefore alkali metals should be avoided and radiation should be kept from reaching the inside of the cathode.

In counting particles, the efficiency G may be computed from eq. (4–3), which we repeat for convenience,

$$G = 1 - e^{-slp} \tag{6–1}$$

where s is the specific ionization of the particle in the gas of the counter, l is the path length and p the pressure of the gas in atmospheres in the counter. To employ this equation presupposes that we know l, the effective path length which the particle travels through the sensitive volume. In the case of coincidence counting, where the path of the particle is determined by other counters, the values of l are known with some accuracy. In single counters, placed so as to be in a beam of particles, the path length may again be known. For single counters exposed to random radiation we must consider the average path length. It is evident that for a cylinder the longest path is diagonally down the length, i.e., $l_{\text{max}} = (d^2 + h^2)^{1/2}$ where d is the diameter and h the length. The minimum path is zero. The exact solution for the general case involves a difficult integration, so that simplifying assumptions or special cases are necessary.

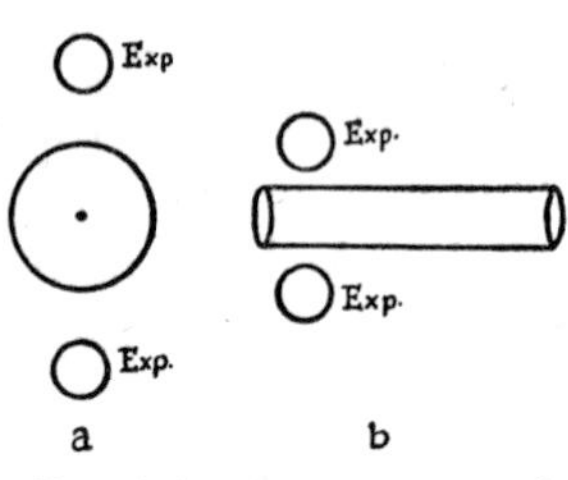

FIG. 6–1. Arrangements of exploring counters to study the distribution of sensitive volume.

Near the ends of the cylinder the field is distorted, and may in places drop below that value required to produce Geiger action. The efficiency of a counter as a function of its length or radius can be measured with the aid of exploring counters as shown in Fig. 6–1a and b, and the distribution of efficiency along its length for a typical counter is shown in Fig. 6–2.

It is evident that our condition, that a single electron will initiate an avalanche, may be vitiated if the electron is captured and does not reach the high field region where the avalanche occurs. Consider two possible causes of electron-removal, recombination and negative ion formation. Recombination may be neglected. The fields are comparatively high, the pressure low, and any electron will become so rapidly removed from the neighborhood of its positive ion that the number recombining will be negligible. As has been shown above, the recombination coefficient (eq. 2–3) and the numerical values cited indicate that recombination is highly improbable in counters.

The effect of negative ion formation may influence the operation of a counter. With gases such as oxygen, the halogens or water vapor present, the probability of electron capture and negative ion formation (see Table 4–2) is not negligible, as we have shown above. The negative ion will drift toward the center wire under the field, and near the wire may either lose the

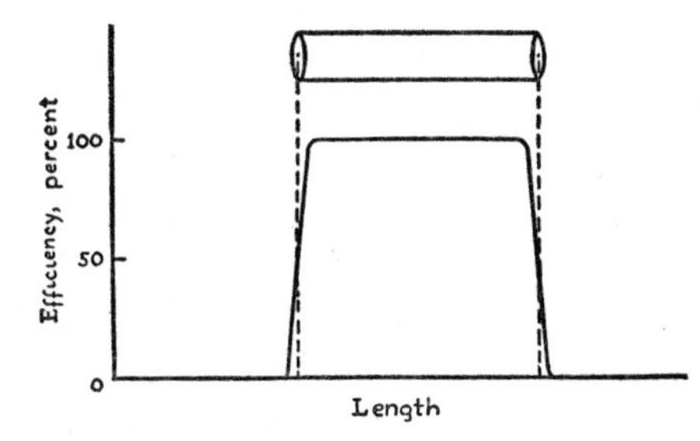

FIG. 6–2. Distribution of efficiency along the length of a typical counter. Data determined using arrangement in Fig. 6–1b.

electron or may acquire enough energy to produce ionization by collision, in other words may start an avalanche. In either case a count is observed. Hence the effect of negative ions is not to reduce the number of counts. What can happen, however, is that a count may be delayed because of the long time required for the negative ion to reach the wire, a time much longer than is needed by an electron. If delayed, then the count may occur (a) after the coincidence circuit has shut off, thereby decreasing the apparent efficiency for counting coincidences, or (b) after the counter has recovered from a count due to an avalanche initiated by some other electron produced in the same ionizing event but not captured, thus producing a spurious count. Either contingency is undesirable and hence gases permitting the formation of negative ions should be avoided.

2. Effects Due to Recovery Time. We assume that the events to be counted occur at random. They are thus assumed to be independent of each other. We may therefore discuss the statistics of random distributions. In this discussion we shall further assume that the intensity, or average number occurring per unit time, is constant. The extension to the special case of a source, the intensity of which varies with time, such as is encountered in measuring radioactive decay, is accomplished by applying the analysis which will follow to each interval of time selected during the variation.

Let $\bar{t}$ be the average time between the arrival of particles, and let $\bar{n}$ be the average number per sec, $\bar{n} = 1/\bar{t}$. Further, let t_r be the recovery time of the counter, such that an event following another by an interval less than t_r will not be counted. Then if $\bar{n}$ counts occur per sec, the counter will be "dead" for a time $\bar{n}t_r$ during that second, or the effective sensitive time t_s of the counter will be

$$t_s = 1 - \bar{n}t_r \tag{6–2}$$

The true counting rate n_t will equal the observed rate n_o plus the number missed n_m during the insensitive time. But the number missed is determined by $\bar{n}t_r$ and hence we may write

$$n_t = n_o/t_s = n_o/(1 - \bar{n}t_r) \tag{6–3}$$

and we note that $\bar{n}$ may be taken as the average observed rate n_o if the number missed is small. Thus, for example, if the actual observed rate n_o is 100 per sec, and the resolving time for this counter is 5×10^{-4} sec, the number missed $n_o t_r$ will be 5×10^{-2}, and $(1 - 5 \times 10^{-2})$ equals 0.95. Hence this counter at this rate is missing 5% of the counts, because it is sensitive only for 95% of the total time.

Consider now that the counts occur at random. We mean by this that the counts are independent, the initial ionizing events are independent, and that the occurrence of one event does not influence the next. Let the probability that a particle will arrive in a time interval dt be adt, a quantity very small compared to unity. Then the probability P_n that n particles arrive in time t when $\bar{n}$ is the average number observed in this time, is given by Poisson's law

$$P_n = ((at)^n/n!)e^{-at} \tag{6-4}$$

The derivation of this law and a discussion of its application in various cases will be found in standard texts on statistics. The problem has been fully discussed by Bateman.[B5] The deviation to be expected of the observed number from the true average is defined as the square root of the mean square of $(\bar{n} - at)$. Thus the deviation D is given by

$$D = \sqrt{at} \tag{6-5}$$

or the deviation is the square root of the total number of counts. If we count 10^4 particles in a unit of time, the deviation will be 100, or in other words our determination of an average number of particles per unit time will have a standard deviation of 1%. The probable error is defined as $0.6745D$, and in the instance cited the probable error will be two-thirds of 1%.

If a counting rate meter is used, the deviation will depend on the time constants of the tank circuit. The analysis has been carried out by Schiff and Evans[S9] who showed that the standard deviation is given by $D = (2XRC)^{-1/2}$, where X is the rate of arrival of pulses, R and C being the resistance and capacity of the tank circuit respectively. Similar fluctuations will be observed in the case of integrating ionization chambers.

Usually counters have a background counting rate, and the counts observed must be distinguished from this background. The background will be due to cosmic radiation and natural radioactive contamination, plus such other stray radiation as may enter the counter. Near any accelerating device, such as a cyclotron, or Van de Graaff machine, there is usually a considerable amount of stray gamma radiation causing background counts. Experimentally, the magnitude of the background is determined by observing the counting rate when no particles to be counted are entering the sensitive volume. This cannot always be done without changing the background, but the magnitude of the background should be determined, even if it be only approximately known. The procedures for applying the corrections we shall next consider.

If the standard deviation of one set of counts is D_1, and for another D_2, then the deviation of the sum or difference will be

$$D = (D_1^2 + D_2^2)^{1/2} \qquad (6\text{–}6)$$

Hence if n_1 counts are produced by the radiation to be detected plus the background and n_2 by the background alone, the standard deviation is

$$D = (n_1 + n_2)^{1/2} \qquad (6\text{–}7)$$

The most difficult rates to determine with accuracy are those which are just detectable above a large background. Thus if a rate of 1000 counts is to be determined against a background of 10,000 counts in the same time, D from (6–7) will be $\sqrt{21{,}000} = 145$ which out of the 1000 to be determined means that the number is known only to 14.5%, while in the same length of time the background can be determined to 1%. Again, if the background is equal to the source, six times as many counts must be measured to achieve a given accuracy as if the background were absent. This is readily seen for, if $n_1 = 2n_2 = 20{,}000$, then $n_2 = 10{,}000$ and $D/n_2 = \sqrt{3n_2}/n_2 = \sqrt{3}/\sqrt{n_2} = 0.01$, whence $n_2 = 3 \times 10^4$ and $n_1 = 6 \times 10^4$, the total number of counts that must be recorded if the background is as assumed, as compared to 10^4 needed in the absence of background. The importance of procedures to reduce background is therefore clear.

3. Errors Due to the Particle Not Reaching the Sensitive Volume. Absorption of the entity being counted in the walls of the counter is the usual cause for the failure of particles to

TABLE 6–1. RELATIVE STOPPING POWER OF VARIOUS MATERIALS FOR α-PARTICLES OF ABOUT 6 MV *

A. Thickness (in mg/cm²) equivalent to 1 cm of air

Substance	Marsden and Richardson	Rosenblum
Al	1.62	1.51
Cu	2.26	2.09
Ag	3.86	2.71
Au	3.96	3.74
Mica	1.45 †	1.43 ‡

B. Atomic stopping power relative to air

Subst.	Geiger	Mano	Subst.	Geiger	Mano
½H_2	0.22	0.20	Cu	2.29	2.57
He	0.42	0.35	Kr	2.89	2.92
Li	0.53	0.50	Mo	2.75	3.20
½N_2	0.98	0.99	Ag	3.04	3.36
½O_2	1.10	1.07	Sn	3.19	3.59
Ne	1.24	1.23	Xe	3.94	3.76
Al	1.40	1.50	Au	4.02	4.50
A	1.92	1.94	Pb	4.25	4.43

C. Atomic stopping power for various velocities (semi-empirical, air = 1)

v(10^9 cm/sec)	1.0	1.5	2.0	2.5	3.0	4.0	5.0
E_α(mv)	2.07	4.66	8.3	12.95	18.6	33.2	51.9
E_H(mv)	0.52	1.17	2.09	3.26	4.70	8.36	13.06
½H_2	0.26	0.224	0.209	0.200	0.194	0.186	0.181
C	0.94	0.932	0.921	0.914	0.908	0.899	0.892
Al	1.45	1.51	1.53	1.54	1.55	1.57	1.59
Cu	(1.92)	2.41	2.62	2.73	2.80	2.89	2.95
Ag	(2.25)	3.08	3.43	3.64	3.76	3.93	4.04
Au	(2.42)	3.96	4.64	5.00	5.25	5.57	5.79

*Atomic stopping power for converting range in the given substance to air equivalent. Data from Livingston and Bethe, *Rev. Mod. Phys.*, **9**, 272 (1937). † Briggs. ‡ Bennett.

reach the sensitive volume. We must therefore consider the range of the particle in the material of which the counter wall (or window) is made. In counting alpha and beta particles, the range of the particle being counted can be obtained from the range curves, Fig. 4–4. The range in air can then be converted to the range in glass by dividing by a factor between 10^3 and 10^4, depending on the type of glass. When a metal window is used, the range can be computed by using the figures for atomic stopping power for the atoms of various elements, listed in Table 6–1. Knowing the thickness of the window, it is possible to estimate whether particles of the type to be counted will reach the interior or what fraction will be absorbed in the process.

When using glass envelope counters to detect neutrons, absorption of neutrons by boron in the glass must be considered. This occurs principally in Pyrex glass which has a high boron content. The fraction H of slow neutrons absorbed in a layer of glass of thickness t cm is given by

$$H = \sigma N \rho P t / \mu \qquad (6\text{–}8)$$

where σ is the capture cross section of boron for the neutrons in question (a function of neutron velocity; see Chapter 3), N is Avogadro's number, ρ is the density of the glass, P is the percentage of boron in the glass and μ is its average atomic weight.

Fast neutrons and cosmic ray mesotrons and gamma rays are not appreciably stopped in the material of which counters are made and may hence be considered as entering the sensitive volume regardless of the construction of the counter.

4. Efficiency of Coincidence Counting. When counters are counting in coincidence, there are two general phenomena which may alter the counting rate and which must be considered. The first is that a particle passing through the coincidence arrangement may not be detected because of an inefficiency in the system. The second is that some event other than that to be detected causes the counters to discharge simultaneously. For example, a large cosmic-ray shower may send particles simultaneously through many counters in various geometrical arrangements.

It is important to know the number of accidental coincidences to be expected when counters are connected for coincidence. If one counter is counting at an average rate of $\bar{n}_1$ per sec and if the resolving time is t, then the chance that a single count will occur during that time will be $\bar{n}_1 t$. If a second counter counts at a rate of $\bar{n}_2$ counts per sec, then the rate of occurrence of accidentals is

$$A_2 = 2\bar{n}_1\bar{n}_2 t \tag{6–9}$$

The factor 2 occurs because of the overlapping of the lengths of time t. Similarly for the threefold coincidences, the accidental rate A_3 for triples will be

$$A_3 = 3\bar{n}_1\bar{n}_2\bar{n}_3 t^2 \tag{6–10}$$

Usually the counters are similar in size and shape and counting rate, and hence we may write for m-fold accidentals

$$A_m = m\bar{n}^m t^{m-1} \tag{6–11}$$

The computations for any special case, such as when one counter is much larger or smaller or counts at a different average rate from the others, is self-evident.

It is evident that the probability of accidental counts is extremely small when (a) the multiplicity m of counters is large, (b) the resolving time is short, and (c) the counters are each counting at a slow rate. Thus for five- or sixfold coincidences, even at high rates of counting such as are found when cosmic-ray counters are operated in the stratosphere, accidentals are almost entirely negligible, providing the resolving time t is small.

The accidental rate for coincidences may be verified experimentally by placing the counters out-of-line, in more or less of a horizontal plane, and far away from each other. In such an arrangement, if no straight line can be drawn through all of them, we will measure only accidentals plus such events as extensive showers which produce ionizing events over a wide area. Extensive showers are quite rare at sea level, occurring perhaps once per hour or even less, depending on the lateral extent. The further the counters are separated, the better is the test.

If only two counters are being tested, and these two are placed in a horizontal plane a considerable distance apart, there will still be a possibility that a single particle could cause both to discharge, causing a "true" coincidence. However, it is much more probable that a single particle will pass through one and will also, as it passes through nearby matter, produce secondaries which will set off the other counter. Thus the arrangement is sensitive to "showers of two" particles. Similarly, if three counters are arranged out-of-line, the arrangement is sensitive to "showers of three," or indeed to the less likely chance that one particle will pass through two and its secondary through the third. The number of "showers of two" greatly exceeds the number of "showers of three" and in general it may be said that the greater the multiplicity the less probable is the event. No general distribution formula can be given because the probability of shower formation is controlled by the distribution of matter in the vicinity of the counters. The number of "showers of two" is much greater in the basement of a building than it is on the roof, due to shower production in the walls and floors of the building.

In any given experiment, the shower correction should be determined. This number of showers will always provide a background which must be added to the random accidentals. Thus the accidental rate for triples is determined by the rate of real doubles occurring simultaneously with random singles, and is larger than eq. (6–10) implies. The shower corrections can be made smaller by two procedures: (a) the use of higher multiplicity coincidences, and (b) the use of suitably disposed anti-coincidence counters as "guard counters" (see Chapter 7). Anti-coincidence counters can be so arranged that showers reaching the main train of counters will have to pass through them and will therefore not be counted. If anti-coincidences are used, the total time that the circuit is insensitive due to the discharge of the anti-coincidence counters must be taken into account if the time-rate of the events being studied is to be determined.

To illustrate this technique, in measuring counter efficiencies it is customary to arrange the counters in a vertical line (see Figs. 6–1 and 6–2). The counting rate of the coincidences of the extreme counters with and without the central counter, whose efficiency is being studied, is then determined. As will be seen from eq. (6–12) below, the efficiency of the counter is the ratio of the counting rates with and without this counter in the circuit. This follows, since the number of counts recorded as double coincidences by the outside pair is $n_2 = nE_2$, where n is the true number of events and E_2 is the efficiency of the two counters in coincidence. The rate of counting triples will then be $n_3 = nE_2E_3$, where E_3 is the efficiency of the third counter. All particles counted by the outside counters must, by the geometry, pass through the middle one. Now this experiment is subject to a shower correction as a "shower of two" can give a false double coincidence. Hence if we use three counters to determine the path, instead of two, the shower correction will be much reduced. Thus we shall measure the ratio of triples to quadruples instead of the ratio of doubles to triples, and thus minimize effects due to "showers of two."

Ordinarily coincidence counting can be done only with penetrating ionizing radiation such as cosmic-ray mesotrons. Alpha and beta particles will not go through most counter-walls and, when electrons or protons are to be counted by coincidence technique, a very thin window must be provided between the counters. The advantage of using coincidence technique is that it helps to eliminate the background due to stray gamma radiation which is so abundantly present near most accelerating devices.

Due to the low efficiency of detection, gamma rays will practically never produce coincidences. It is evident that if the efficiency of a counter is E_1, of another E_2 and so on, then the efficiency of a combination will be

$$E_m = E_1E_2E_3 \tag{6–12}$$

and, if the efficiencies are equal,

$$E_m = E^m$$

Since the efficiency of a gamma ray counter may be 10^{-4}, the occurrence even of double coincidences is rare. A similar argument holds for fast neutrons, since the recoil efficiency is so small (see Chapter 3).

Slow neutrons cannot be used in coincidence work since the neutron disappears in the act of producing the disintegration which is detected.

Coincidences between proportional counters and Geiger counters can be measured. The circuits are described in Chapter 7, and the efficiency of any arrangement, once the efficiency of the proportional counter is shown, is given by eq. (6–12).

5. Errors in Using Proportional Counters. In general, proportional counters will give pulses depending on the amount of energy liberated in ionization in the primary ionizing event, and also depending on the gas amplification A, as in eq. (3–1). The possible errors in interpreting the results may arise from (a) the range of the particle not lying entirely in the sensitive volume, or being interrupted by the particle striking the wall of the counter, (b) the background of large pulses due to alpha particles and giant showers, and (c) any effects such as electron capture which cause an apparent decrease in A.

The resolving time of proportional counters is also of the order of 10^{-4} sec. The travel time of the positive ions and the appropriate calculations of the effects of this time have already been given. There is, however, one feature which should be mentioned. That is that the avalanche in a proportional discharge is not as fully developed as that in a Geiger discharge. The avalanche may not spread down the entire length of the wire. Hence there may be portions of the wire which will be sensitive and may support another avalanche before the first is terminated. Consequently it is possible, if

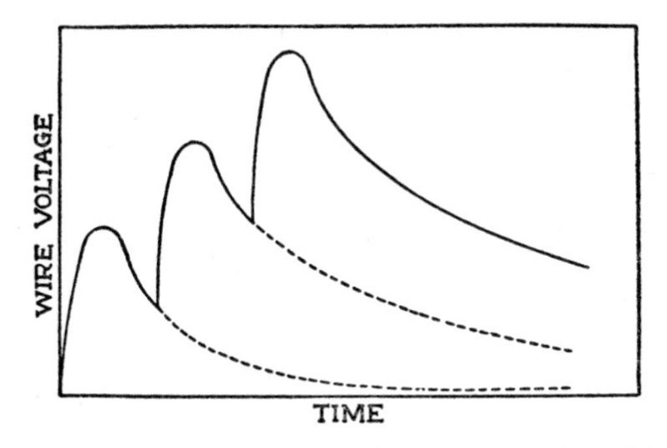

FIG. 6–3. Multiple counts in a proportional counter occurring within the recovery time of the counter. Normal pulse recovery indicated by dotted line.

the *RC* time of the central wire of the counter is short (say 10^{-5} to 10^{-6} sec), to have pulses superposed on one another and pulses occurring with spacings less than the resolving time needed to complete a pulse. Since proportional counters are usually operated at comparatively slow counting rates, this problem does not often arise, but at fast rates the potential of the wire may show various spurts in quick succession superposed on one another. The true "dead time" of a proportional counter is therefore less than that of a Geiger counter. The fact that the changing potential of the wire will cause A to vary for counts which overlap, should be borne in mind if pulse size distributions obtained at fast counting rates are to be interpreted with precision. The graph of the voltage variation of the wire is shown in Fig. 6–3. Because of the functioning of the space charge sheath, this phenomenon takes place only with proportional counters and not in the Geiger region.

The amount of ionization produced in the primary ionizing event must be formed in the sensitive volume to be effective. A particle which passes entirely through the counter or which collides with one of the walls will produce a correspondingly smaller pulse. The heaviest amount of ionization is produced near the end of the range. Consequently it is important to know not only the geometrical length of the range of the particle in the gas of the counter, but what portion (i.e., whether beginning, middle or end) of the range lies within the sensitive volume. Thus, for example, an alpha particle gives up 1.9 Mev in ionization in the last centimeter of its range, but only 0.7 Mev in 1 cm, 5 to 6 cm from the end of the range. If the counter is filled to 0.1 atm pressure with a gas whose stopping power is about the equivalent of that of air, and has a 10 cm average path through the sensitive volume, then the amount of energy in ionization produced in 1 cm of range in air (at STP) will appear in the counter. The expected pulse size can be computed now if we know what portion of the range is involved. Thus the expected pulse size depends on the nature and pressure of the gas and on the geometry of the path through the counter, and each case should be computed separately.

Proportional counters will exhibit a background of large pulses, which must be considered in interpreting the results. There are two chief agencies producing such large pulses. The first is the natural radioactive contamination of all substances. This contamination manifests itself by the emission of alpha particles into the sensitive volume. Most of these originate in the walls of the counter, as reasonably pure gas has a comparatively low radioactive content. A well cleaned surface, which has not had undue exposure to contamination, should show of the order of 10^{-4} alpha particle per sq cm per minute. Normal variations are large and may differ from the figure stated by a factor of ten in either direction. If the material of which the counter is made has been left around in some of the older laboratories in which radium or its products have at one time been used, the contamination is likely to be much greater. Similarly, some elements acquire long period radioactivities by prolonged exposure to neutrons and, for example, copper which has been stored in a room adjoining a cyclotron may have undesirable activity. The insides of ionization chambers are often painted with very pure carbon black to reduce the alpha background, and this can be done in counters although it is not often worth while.

The other cause of large pulses is cosmic radiation. Occasionally the core of a giant shower will strike a measuring device, and literally many thousands of electrons will traverse the sensitive volume simultaneously. Large amounts of ionization are thus liberated and a big pulse appears on the wire. This effect is not very large at sea level, usually only a few per day, but increases rapidly with elevation. In general no shielding is effective in reducing these showers. The number of such giant showers is, however, constant at any one place and can hence be determined and allowed for. Similarly, the alpha background is constant and need but be determined once for each instrument.

The expected value of A is not realized in every case. Suppose that an ionizing event takes place at some distance from the wire, and that electron-capture to form negative ions takes place. If some of the electrons are withdrawn and do not reach the region in which the avalanche is started, the total avalanche size will be smaller. Any negative ions formed will reach the wire or will shed their electrons near the wire long after the first avalanche due to electrons is over, and consequently will not contribute to the size of the initial pulse. Since the halogens are sufficiently electronegative to exhibit appreciable electron capture, we might expect that this phenomenon would manifest itself in BF_3 neutron counters. Indeed, Brubaker and Pollard [B6] found that the size of a pulse produced by a primary ionizing event of constant size depended on how far out from the wire the event occurred. They attribute the effect to electron capture. That this is probably not the only factor involved is seen from the fact that they find appreciable dependence on the radius also for some gases in which electron capture may be supposed negligible such as argon and hydrogen.

Another cause of an apparently lower A is the phenomenon of partial paralysis exhibited by proportional counters when operating with a very high beta or gamma ray background. Since in these circumstances numerous small avalanches will continuously be taking place, numerous positive ion groups will be migrating out toward the cylinder, and the result will be a lowering of the field in the counter. The value of A will therefore be reduced. The Montgomerys [M7] have observed a reduction in the number of large counts which are recorded under these conditions.

It may be well to repeat here that, in BF_3 counters when the disintegration produced by slow neutrons takes place, two particles are formed. One is an alpha, the other a recoiling lithium nucleus. They travel in opposite directions. Thus if one hits the wall, the other goes out into the gas. The pulse produced will of course be larger if both particles end their range in the gas, but even if only one component is effective, the amount of ionization produced is still considerably larger than that produced by beta particles.

6. Procedures To Insure Short Recovery Times. The analysis which we have given above presupposes that only one recovery time need be considered. If the mechanical recorder has a much longer recovery time than the counter, it will miss counts to which the counter responds. It is therefore important that the recovery time of the counter be the longest time constant in the entire arrangement.

In the case of non-selfquenching counters, the recovery time is determined by the RC of the quenching resistance if the counter is resistance quenched, or by that of the circuit if electronic quenching is used. As has been indicated elsewhere, *RC* quenching times are usually of the order of 10^{-2} to 10^{-3} sec. An electronic quenching circuit can operate satisfactorily in 10^{-4} sec but not much less, the limitation being attributable to the discharge mechanism. If the electronic quenching circuit is made with too short a time constant, the counter will not be completely quenched and the entire arrangement may indeed break into oscillation. We specifically except from this discussion the potential reversing circuits which are treated separately.

Selfquenching counters recover in the time determined by the ion-sheath mobility. This again is of the order of 10^{-3} to 10^{-4} sec. The amplifiers connected to any counter can easily be given time constants of 10^{-5} sec or so by choosing appropriate coupling *RC* values. The recovery times of amplifiers so designed may be neglected as they are smaller than that of the counter and do not affect the result.

Mechanical recorders are usually the slowest element in a counter circuit. Some will follow a 60 cycle AC wave, and have time constants of the order of 10^{-2} sec, but few are faster. Therefore scaling circuits (see Chapter 7) are recommended, and must be used for fast counting. A scaling circuit not only slows down the average counting rate to an interval which the recorder can follow but also improves the statistics in that the output pulses are more regularly spaced and hence the probability of close doubles is decreased. Since the recovery time of a scaling circuit can also be made short compared to that of the counter, this time also may be neglected. In ionization chambers, where the ion-collecting time is sometimes long, the fundamental limitation may be in the chamber and the recovery time of even a slow recorder may be neglected.

To summarize, for minimum errors in fast counting: (1) the recovery time of the amplifier must be short and (2) a scaling circuit should precede the mechanical recorder. The recovery time of the entire arrangement will then be determined by that of the counter, and the appropriate corrections may be made.

7. Interpretation of Counting Rate Data *a. Statistical tests.* The discussion of statistics which we have given above may be made the basis for ascertaining whether a counter is behaving properly. Suppose, for example, a counter is suspected of having spurious counts. The following simple procedure will throw light on its operation.

First the counter is adjusted to detect the radiation desired. Then the number of counts occurring in each minute is recorded. This observation is continued for about half an hour, thus giving some thirty numbers. If the counting rate is high, a time interval shorter than a minute may be used. The results are then tabulated. The average counting rate is determined. The standard deviation is next computed from the data. The standard deviation should, by eq. (6–5), be the square root of the number of counts. If the standard deviation differs appreciably from this figure, the presumption is strong that the events being counted are not at random. For example, spurious counts such as would be produced by negative ions would follow the true count at short intervals. The resulting standard deviation calculated from the data would then be less than that obtained by taking the square root of the number of counts.

b. Significance of counting rate curves. Any given recording circuit, unless it is provided with a special arrangement to eliminate large pulses, will count all pulses greater than a certain minimum size. This minimum size is determined by the characteristics of the circuit (see Chapter 7) or by the "bias" or "cutoff" of the amplifier used. The curve of counting rate as a function of voltage is therefore an integral curve and continually increases. Should the counting rate decrease beyond a certain voltage, it is an indication that some sort of paralysis or saturation is taking place in the counter or in the attached electronic circuit. The data obtained on such a curve above the point where it starts to decrease should be interpreted with caution. A counter should not be operated in the region where the characteristic has a negative slope, in ordinary circumstances, as this can be due to excessive overvoltage, which may damage the counter.

The characteristic curve of counting rate as a function of voltage determines the total number of counts, N, greater than a certain size (E_{min}), as indicated by

$$N \Big|_{E_{\text{min}}}^{E_{\text{max}}} = \int_{E_{\text{min}}}^{E_{\text{max}}} N(E)dE \tag{6-13}$$

where the upper limit E_{max} is usually practically infinite. The pulse size distribution is then given by

$$N(E)dE \tag{6-14}$$

which may be defined as the number of counts of size (or energy) lying between E and $E + dE$. This pulse size distribution may therefore be determined by differentiation, with respect to energy, of the integral counting rate curve. Thus, for example, two groups of particles of different sizes (say a few contamination alpha particles and a lot of electrons) would give rise to a curve of counting rate as a function of voltage which would have two "steps" in it. Another illustration is the normal "plateau" curve of a Geiger counter which, if flat, means that all the pulses are of the same size at any one voltage and that no new or spurious counts occur as the voltage is raised. Either the differentiation or the integration may be done graphically. The accuracy usually decreases in such graphical operations. For a discussion of procedures, the reader is referred to the standard texts on statistics, such as *Treatment of Experimental Data*, by Worthing and Geffner, Wiley, 1943.

CHAPTER 7

AUXILIARY ELECTRONIC CIRCUITS

A. Introduction

The counter discharge produces a voltage pulse on the central wire system, and it is the purpose of the auxiliary electronic circuits to measure, record or control this pulse. As we have mentioned before, the pulse is of about 10^{-4} sec duration and is therefore too short to operate many of the currently available recording devices. On the other hand, the pulse produced by a Geiger counter is often of considerable size, being in general of the order of the overvoltage in amplitude. A pulse of 100 to 200 volts amplitude is not uncommon. It is evident, therefore, that such pulses are sufficiently large to operate most vacuum tubes and do not require further amplification, but may require broadening or lengthening. The pulses formed by a proportional counter, on the other hand, may be quite small and may require considerable amplification. A pulse of 10^{-4} volt from such a counter is not unusual, and high gain circuits are required to render such a pulse capable of operating recording equipment.

Almost without exception, counters are operated with the central wire positive and the cylinder negative. The voltage sources supplying such a counter may have either the positive or the negative side gounded, depending entirely upon convenience. The circuits appropriate to operation with either the central wire system or the cylinder of the counter at ground potential are shown in Fig. 7–1A and B. In the case of counters in which the cylinder also serves as the external envelope, it is desirable to operate the cylinder at ground potential (Fig. 7–1B). In these circumstances the cylinder may be safely handled while the high voltage is on. In addition the central wire system is electrostatically shielded. In those counters employing an outer envelope of glass or other insulating ma-

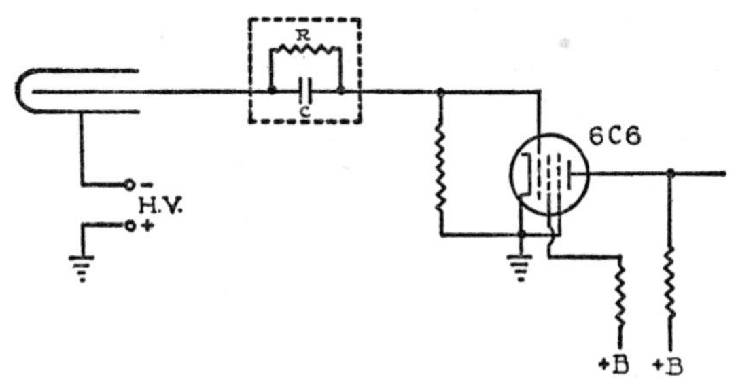

FIG. 7–1A. Fundamental counter circuit for negative high voltages. Wire at ground potential. Dotted condenser and quenching resistor omitted with selfquenching counters.

terial, it is often useful to have the central wire system at essentially ground potential (Fig. 7–1A). The cylinder, in the latter case, is operated at a high negative potential with respect to ground. The advantage of the latter system is that it eliminates the necessity for the blocking condenser which must be a good insulator and must have a high leakage resistance.

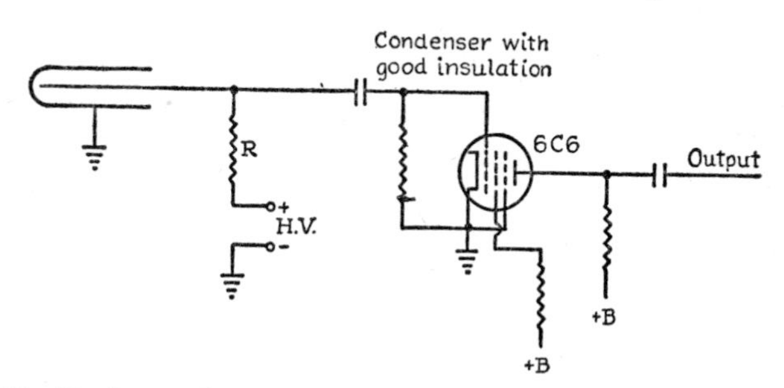

FIG. 7–1B. Fundamental counter circuit for positive high voltages. Cylinder at ground potential.

Some of the circuit diagrams shown below are in schematic form, without constants. This is done since the constants depend on the characteristics of the particular tubes used. The justification of particular values lies outside the scope of this text. As anyone familiar with such circuits knows, a few of the constants are critical, but most may be widely varied without interfering with the operation of the circuit. One laboratory may have available powerpacks producing 400 volts; another may have similar sets producing 325 or 250 volts. The resistances in scaling circuits, integrating circuits and other devices will have to be adapted accordingly. It would be erroneous to imply that a given circuit will work only on one set of voltages and circuit constants. Usually, if specific voltages are available, or if particular vacuum tubes are at hand, the constants can readily be modified to suit the circumstances. Similarly, wide variations in tube types are usually possible. When substituting new tube types, the "resistance-coupled amplifier" section of the standard receiving tube manuals will be found helpful. British experimenters may prefer to use Mullard or Osram triodes instead of RCA pentodes in several of the circuits shown below. Conversely, pentodes may be substituted for triodes with good results in other cases. Such constants as are given in the diagrams should be regarded, not as the only possible values, but rather as the starting point for testing. Any new circuit should be built the first time on a "breadboard" so that various circuit constants and experimental rearrangements can be readily tried. Experimentation and trial of various values and arrangements is to be preferred to rigid insistence on unnecessarily detailed "cookbook" specifications.

B. Quenching Circuits

Non-selfquenching counters require the use of a quenching arrangement which may be either a high resistance or an electronic circuit. These circuits may be dispensed with in the case of the selfquenching counters. The objection to using a high resistance is, as we have pointed out above, that a long time constant is introduced into the circuit. Since it is not practical to reduce the value of the resistance sufficiently to provide a short time constant, it is therefore customary to employ an electronic circuit which performs this function. Several such circuits are shown in Fig. 7–2.

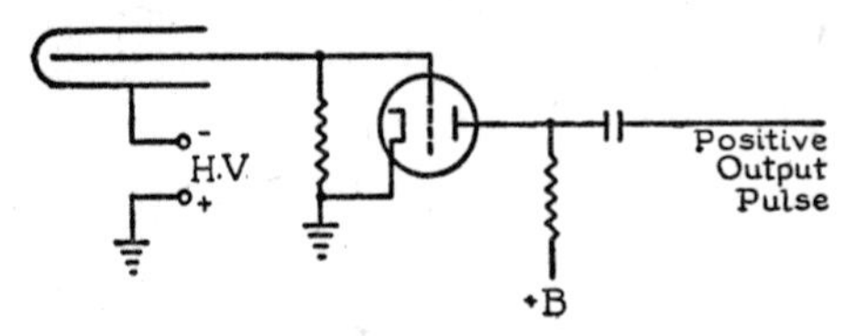

FIG. 7–2A(1). Modified Neher and Pickering quenching circuit to give positive output pulse.

It must be recalled that the fundamental limitation on the time of recovery of a non-selfquenching counter is determined by the mobilities of the positive ions in the counter itself. The several quenching circuits therefore are also governed by this limit. If the time constants of the circuits are made much less than 10^{-4} sec, the counter itself will not have ceased to discharge and the entire arrangement will not operate satisfactorily. Thus these circuits may reduce the quenching time from, say, 10^{-2} second for a resistance-quenched counter

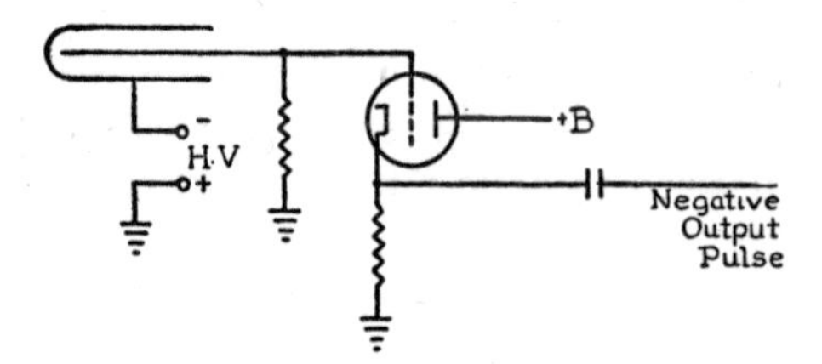

FIG. 7–2A(2). Modified Neher and Pickering quenching circuit to give negative output pulse.

($R = 10^9$ ohms, $C = 10^{-11}$ farad) to a figure near 10^{-4} sec, but will not operate at still shorter times.

Fig. 7–2A(1) shows a quenching circuit devised by Neher and Pickering.[N1] In this circuit, a negative pulse from the counter wire arrives on the grid of the tube. Since the grid of the tube is connected through a resistance to the cathode, the tube is normally in a conducting state and the grid and counter wire are approximately at cathode potential. The arrival of a negative pulse on the grid causes the tube to become non-conducting, and the grid is effectively isolated for an instant. Thus the high potential is, in effect, removed from the counter during this time. The counter wire and grid recover with a *RC* time constant characterized by the resistance of the grid leak and the distributed capacity of the counter wire and grid

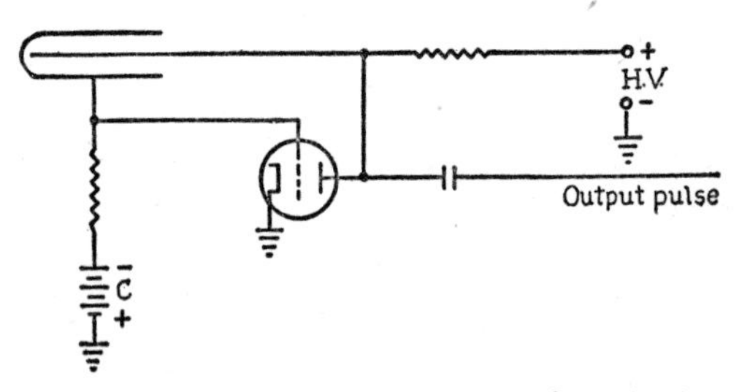

FIG. 7–2B. Neher and Harper quenching circuit.

system. If we take this distributed capacity to be of the order of 10^{-11} farad and use a 10 megohm grid leak, the counter will recover in 10^{-4} sec. It is evident that a positive pulse will appear in the plate circuit of the tube as indicated. This pulse may then be fed into the subsequent scaling or recording circuits. If it is desired to have a negative pulse to feed into the next stage, this may be accomplished by the modification shown in Fig. 7–2A(2). In this circuit the load resistance of the tube is placed in the cathode line instead of in the plate circuit, and the sign of the pulse therefore reverses. The chief disadvantage of this circuit is that, since the tube is conducting, a constant drain is put on the high voltage supply.

The second type of quenching circuit was devised by Wynn-Williams [W3] and later independently developed by Neher and Harper.[N2] This arrangement is shown in Fig. 7–2B. In this circuit it will be observed that the grid is held at a negative potential by the C battery, and that therefore the tube is normally in a non-conducting state. When the counter counts, the cylinder of the counter swings to a positive value. This causes the tube to conduct, and the plate current passing through the plate resistor R_p produces a voltage drop which is effectively subtracted from the high voltage. Thus the vacuum tube partially short-circuits the counter, or in other words removes part of its potential. If the gain of the tube is μ then the effective resistance of the tube is μR_g when the

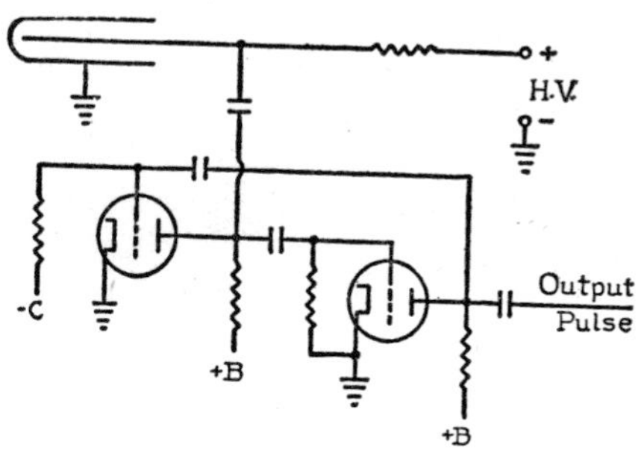

FIG. 7–2C. Multivibrator quenching circuit devised by Getting.

tube is conducting. The recovery of the system is again controlled by the *RC* time constant of the grid circuit and may be made of the order of 10^{-4} sec as in the previous case. The disadvantage of this system is that the entire high voltage is connected across the vacuum tube. Most receiving tubes are sufficiently well insulated so that they will not break down, but the useful life of the tube is often short and occasionally flash-overs occur.

The third type of circuit is the multivibrator arrangement devised by Getting [G7] and shown in Fig. 7–2C. In this circuit one tube of a multivibrator is biased negatively so that it is normally in a stable state with one tube conducting and the other cut off by the bias. The arrival of a negative pulse from the central wire of the counter system causes the multivibrator to go through one cycle of its oscillation. The final act in this oscillation is the arrival of a considerable charge from the plate of the second tube through the condenser onto the grid and counter wire system. The counter wire is thus driven to a potential below its normal operating voltage, and the discharge consequently ceases. The recovery of this system depends on the time constants of the multivibrator and in particular on the grid condensers and resistors. Again, this system can be made to operate in about 10^{-4} sec, the fundamental limit being again not in the circuit but in the positive ion collection time in the counter.

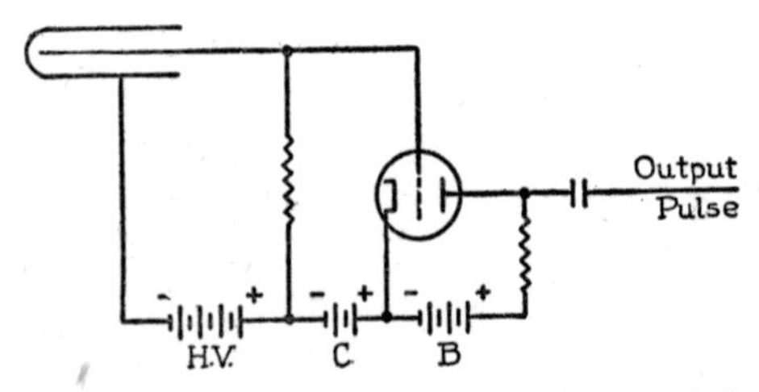

FIG. 7–2D. Modification of circuits shown in Figs. 7–2A and B to be completely floating or grounded at any one desired point.

A modification of these circuits (Fig. 7–2D) has been found useful in connection with radiosonde cosmic-ray balloon observations. This circuit was devised by Johnson,[J1] and was used by Johnson and Korff [J2] in a series of balloon flights. In these flights economy of battery weight was essential. In this circuit the plate voltage of the quenching tube is added to the high voltage supply. The plate battery is thus made to perform a double function. The operation of the circuit is essentially identical with that described above in the circuit in Fig. 7–2A.

Still further modification of this circuit is that made by Wynn-Williams,[W4] in which a single thyratron performs the dual function of extinguishing the discharges and causing a recording counter to record. This circuit is shown in Fig. 7–2E. In this circuit, the thyratron grid is normally held at a negative potential by the C battery, and the thyratron is normally non-conducting. The potential across the counter is therefore the sum of the voltages of the high voltage battery plus the B battery plus the C battery. When a count occurs, the cylinder of the counter swings to a more positive value and the grid of the thyratron becomes positive, thus permitting the thyratron to conduct. The flow of plate current causes the recorder relay to open, thus simultaneously recording a count and extinguishing the discharge in the thyratron by breaking

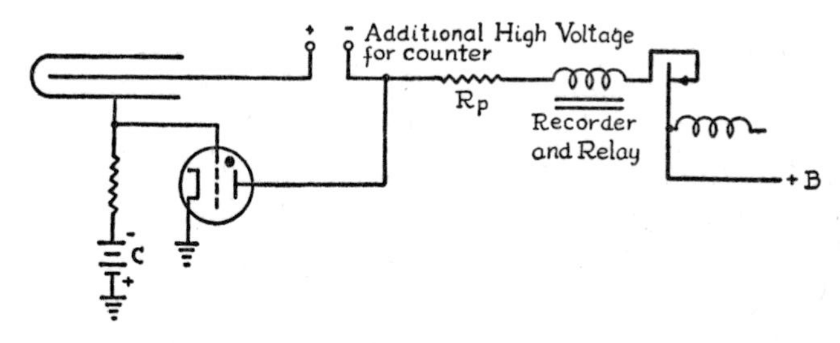

FIG. 7–2E. Combined quenching and recording circuit using a thyratron.

its plate circuit and permitting the negative grid to resume control. This same break effectively removes the potential from the counter, which then recovers. The recovery time of this circuit is controlled by the speed of the recording unit. The chief objection to this type of circuit is that, as with the Neher-Pickering circuit, the counter cylinder is floating, and further, that the entire high voltage supply must be kept at some potential above ground.

C. Coincidence Circuits

One of the most important uses of counters has been made possible through coincidence technique. Coincidence circuits permit imposition, on an arrangement of counters, of the condition that the counters must discharge simultaneously or within an assignable time interval of each other. Thus it is possible to determine the direction in which a particle is traveling by the use of two or more counters connected in coincidence and arranged in line.* Multiple coincidences permit analysis of the complex ionizing events encountered in cosmic radiation and nuclear physics in which an ionizing ray may be followed as it traverses matter and generates secondary particles with various characteristics. The part played by non-ionizing radiation may also be studied by the aid of anti-coincidence devices.

1. Normal Coincidence Arrangements. The simplest type of coincidence circuit is that devised by Rossi in 1929.[R2] With this circuit it is possible to record coincidence due to any number of counters, triples and quadruples being commonly recorded, but the circuit will operate satisfactorily on tenfold or even greater coincidences. The circuit is shown for triple coincidences in Fig. 7–3A. If additional identical branches are desired, all plates are connected together. The circuit is shown connected for resistance-quenched, non-selfquenching counters. For selfquenching counters the resistance R and condenser C are omitted. The essential feature of this circuit is that all of the plates of the tube are tied together, and connected through a common resistor to the B supply. The grids of all the tubes are connected to the cathodes so that the tubes are conducting. When a negative pulse arrives on the grid of any tube, it ceases to conduct and the tube therefore becomes a high resistance, whereas it was a much lower resistance while it was conducting. The potential of the common plate circuit is therefore determined by the equivalent of a system of parallel resistances. If all the tubes but one become non-conducting, or in other words become high resistances because of the arrival of negative pulses on their respective grids, we will have a circuit in which

* Another method of obtaining directional indication has been devised by B. Rajewski (*Zeits. f. Phys.* **120**, 627 (1943) who made use of asymmetric electron emission first reported by Bragg & Madsen (*Phil. Mag.* **16**, 918 (1908)). Thus if a counter cylinder is made half of lead and half of aluminum, more electrons are ejected by gamma rays entering lead, and leaving aluminum.

there will be several high resistances in parallel with one low resistance. Since most of the current will flow through the low resistance, the change in potential of the plate circuit will be small. If on the other hand all tubes cease to conduct, the change in potential of this plate circuit becomes considerable. A large pulse therefore occurs in the output only when all tubes simultaneously cease to conduct. The circuit can therefore re-

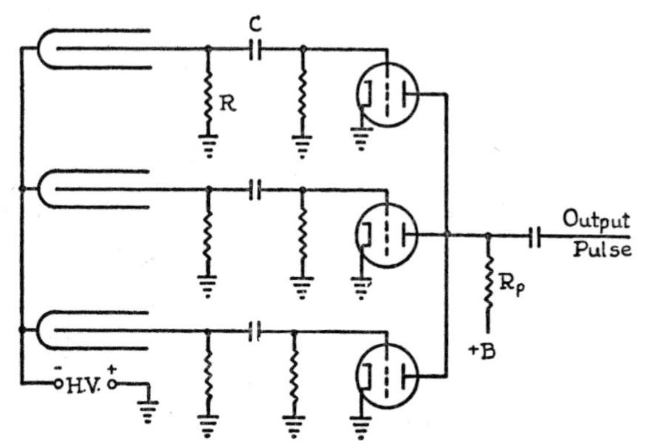

FIG. 7–3A. The conventional Rossi coincidence circuit. With selfquenching counters, *R* and *C* are omitted.

cord coincidences between the discharges of any number of counters. For example, the resistance of a 6C6, when it is conducting, may be 10^5 ohms, whereas it may exceed 10^8 when it is not conducting. Let R_p in Fig. 7–3A be 10^6 ohms, and let the *B* potential be 200 volts. The potential of the common plates will therefore be +6.6 volts when the three tubes are conducting, i.e., when no counts have taken place. Let two tubes but not the third count, and the potential becomes +22 volts; but let all three count and the potential becomes +198 volts. Thus we have a pulse of only 14 volts for an incomplete, as compared to 192 volts for a complete, coincidence.

The resolving time of the circuit is determined by the *RC* time constants of the coupling condensers and plate and grid resistors. Short resolving times are often desired to minimize accidentals. Times of the order of five microseconds may be obtained by using condensers of 0.00005 microfarad and resistors of 10^5 ohms. This time is shorter than that required by the counter to recover, and only the sharp initial "break" of the counter discharge curve is used. However, accidentals are greatly reduced by this procedure. The ultimate limit on resolving times is caused by the intrinsic time-lags of the counters themselves.

Another system for recording coincidences is also possible through the use of a multiple grid tube. Such a circuit is

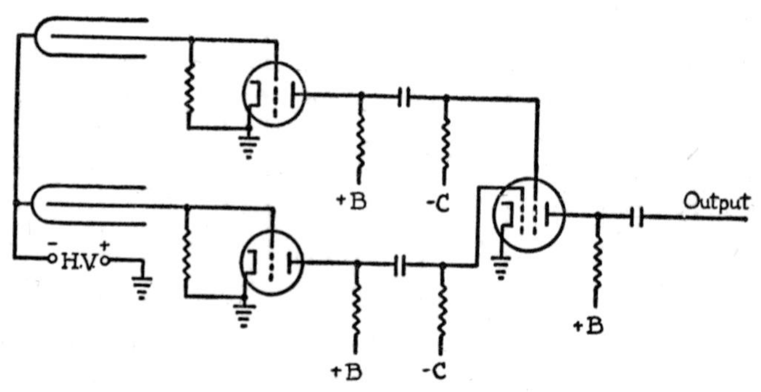

FIG. 7–3B. Mixing circuit for multiple grid tubes.

shown in Fig. 7–3B. Here the several grids are held at a negative potential by a C battery, and the tube becomes conducting only when a positive pulse is applied simultaneously to all of the grids. Such positive pulses may be obtained either directly from the cylinders of the counters or through an intermediate stage of vacuum tubes, as shown in the diagram. The intermediate tubes may be quenching tubes, and thus non-self-quenching counters may be used with this arrangement. The multiplicity of the coincidences is limited by the number of nearly electrically identical grids in the mixing tube.

2. Anti-Coincidence Circuits. It is sometimes important to impose upon an arrangement of counters the condition that one or more tubes shall not count while other tubes are counting. This arrangement adds one degree of flexibility to counter circuits and permits important advances in the analyses which can be made therewith, since it is possible to establish that when one thing happens something else does not happen. Thus, for example, it is sometimes desirable to know that a ray traversing an arrangement of counters is a single ray and is not a portion of a multiple-ray shower. An illustration of an arrangement of counters in coincidence (*C*) and anti-coincidence (*A*) is shown in Fig. 7–3E(1). Here we see that the counters *C* define a path through the absorber. Any simultaneous shower rays or non-collimated particles will trip the guard counters in anti-coincidence *A* at the side and the event would not be recorded.

Also, for example, it may be desirable to ascertain whether a given ray has stopped in an absorber. The arrangement shown in Fig. 7–3E(2) will insure the above condition. Here the three counters *C* determine that a particle has passed into the absorber, and the fact that the anti-coincidence counter *A* does not count proves that the particle did not come out in the downward direction. The importance of high efficiency in the anti-coincidence counters is self-evident, for even a 98% efficiency might render the interpretation of such an experiment ambiguous.

If we consider the operation of a simple coincidence circuit, the electrical requirement of the anti-coincidence circuit becomes evident. In general, negative pulses are fed into a set of Rossi coincidence tubes, and the swing in the plate circuit will be large if all of the tubes receive a negative pulse simultaneously. If a pulse of the opposite sign arrives simultaneously in the plate circuit of the mixing stage, then no coincidence will be registered. All that is necessary to introduce such a pulse is the addition of one vacuum tube which reverses the sign of the pulse going through it. Anti-coincidence circuits were used by Swann and Ramsey in the equipment carried aloft during the stratosphere flight of the balloon "Explorer II" in 1936. Similar circuits have been published by Herzog [H2] and have been used by many observers. A simple schematic arrangement for this type of device is shown in Fig. 7–3C, in which it will be seen that the counter which operates as an anti-coincidence counter has one more vacuum tube in its control circuit. The pulse produced by this counter is therefore fed into the mixing stage reversed in sign as compared to those produced by the other counters, and the large plate swing

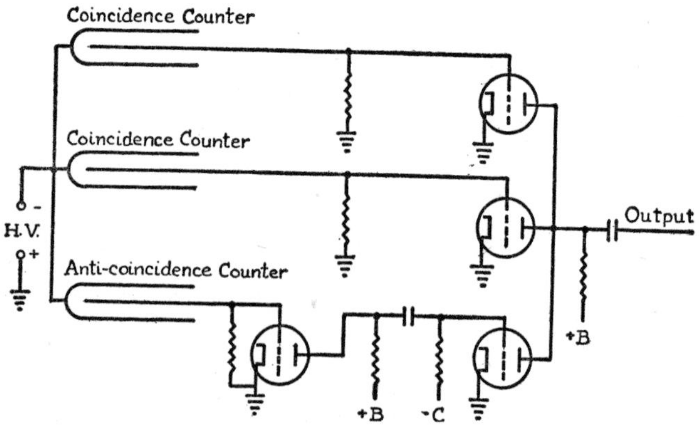

Fig. 7–3C. Anti-coincidence circuit, selfquenching counter shown.

which causes the Rossi circuit to record coincidence is thereby nullified. It should be added that, since a positive pulse must be introduced into the grid of the mixing tube to record anti-coincidences, therefore the grid of this tube must have a negative bias rendering it non-conducting. If no pulse appears on its grid, the remainder of the circuit functions to give normal coincidences. In general, the arrangement can be adapted to an indefinite number of tubes, and it is possible to have many tubes in coincidence and many in anti-coincidence.

3. Coincidences between Proportional Counters and Geiger Counters. In certain investigations it is desirable to measure the coincident discharge of Geiger counters and proportional counters. Thus, for example, it is possible to measure the specific ionization of a given ray by the arrangement shown in Fig. 7–3F(1). In this arrangement a coincident discharge of the three Geiger counters and the proportional counter proves that a ray has passed through the proportional counter P along a definite and well collimated path. The size of the pulse in the proportional counter may be measured simultaneously and independently by an additional circuit (see below), thus mak-

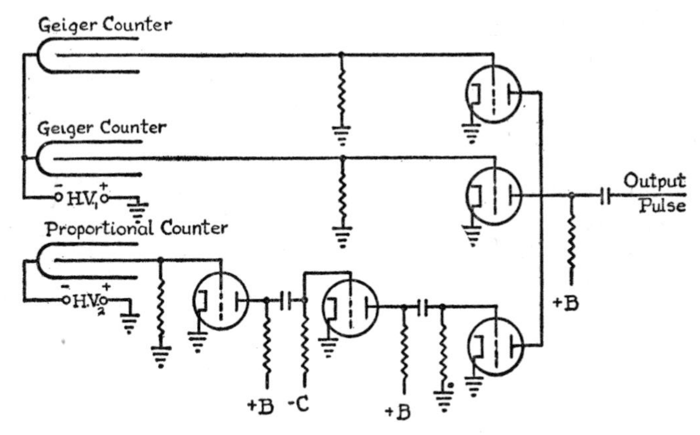

FIG. 7–3D. Circuit for coincidences between Geiger counters and proportional counter. Separate high voltage supplies are shown as the operating potentials are often different.

ing use of condition of coincidence as well as recording the amplitude of the pulse which produces that coincidence.

Another arrangement in which the proportional counter and Geiger counters are used in coincidence was employed to study the association between neutron and showers.[K10] The neutron counter was a proportional counter of the boron-trifluoride type described in Chapter 3, and was adjusted so as not to be sensitive to electrons. A tray of Geiger counters was arranged below it. Thus, the simultaneous discharge of the Geiger and neutron counters established that (a) shower took place and (b) a large ionizing event such as produced by a neutron occurred in the neutron counter. The counter arrangement is shown in Fig. 7–3F(2), where N represents the (proportional) neutron counter and the horizontal array of Geiger counters C below it represent the shower-detecting arrangement. Since the neutron may be slowed down to a velocity at which it can be detected more efficiently in perhaps 10^{-4} sec, it is desirable not to have the resolving time of the circuit (Fig. 7–3D) too short. This is readily accomplished by making the RC times of the grid-plate coupling resistors and condensers of the desired values. For example, a 10^6 ohm resistor and a 0.0001 microfarad condenser will serve the purpose.

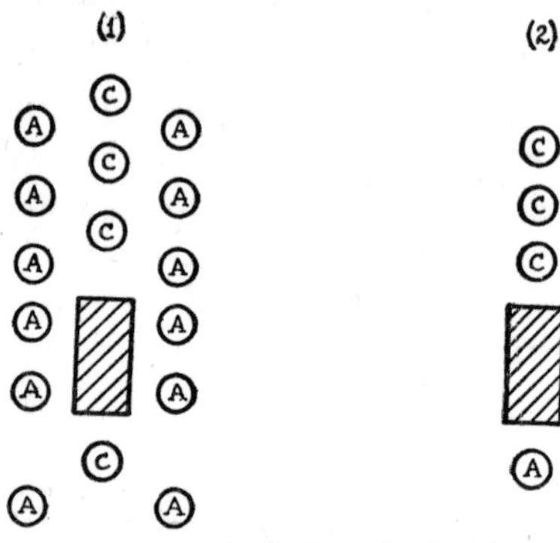

FIG. 7–3E. Typical anti-coincidence arrangements. (1) Employs anti-coincidence counters A as guard counters to assure that the counters C are not set off by showers from the side. (2) Insures that a particle having passed through C is absorbed and does not emerge in the direction determined by C.

The electrical procedure employed to determine coincidences between Geiger counters and proportional counters must take account of the fact that the pulses due to the proportional counters are usually much smaller than those due to Geiger

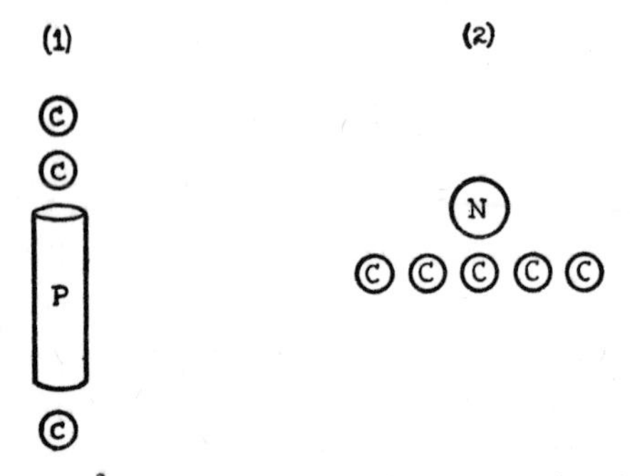

FIG. 7–3F. Typical counter arrangements using counters in coincidence with proportional counters. (1) The counters C define a path for particles through the proportional counter P. (2) Coincidences between neutrons (N) and showers C are counted.

counters. It is therefore usually desirable to have additional stages of amplification preceding the mixing stage. Since negative pulses are added in the mixing stage, and since the proportional counter gives a negative pulse, an even number of additional stages of amplification must be used. For most problems, two stages suffice. The suitable circuit arrangement in this case is shown in Fig. 7–3D. The counters are shown supplied by a common high voltage source but independent supplies are used if the proportional and Geiger counters operate at different voltages. Selfquenching Geiger counters are assumed in the circuit as shown.

D. Scaling Circuits

In many experiments with counters it is important to use scaling circuits for the purpose of scaling the impulses down to slower counting rates. This procedure is useful when the counting rate of the counter exceeds the rate which the mechanical recorder can follow and, further, it improves the statistics. The occurrence of closely spaced double counts is highly probable on statistical grounds even in the case of comparatively slow counting rates. These close doubles would be registered as a single count by a comparatively slow mechanical recorder even though the circuit appeared to be counting properly.

1. Vacuum Tube Scaling Circuits. The general principle of scaling circuits in use at the present time is that embodied in the trigger circuit developed by Eccles and Jordan in 1918.[E1] An arrangement of two triodes is possible, which has a characteristic curve in which a portion exhibits a negative slope. Since the negative slope portion of the curve is unstable, the circuit is able to change suddenly from one stable state to the other. A typical circuit diagram employing an arrangement of this sort is shown in Fig. 7–4A. If the potentials and resistances are correctly chosen, one of the tubes will be conducting and the other non-conducting. The plate current of the tube which is conducting flows through its plate resistance and also through the grid resistor of the other tube. The *IR* drop through this resistance is such as to keep the grid of the second tube negative and thus to render it non-conducting. It is evident that this state is stable and that the tubes will remain in this state indefinitely. If now a positive pulse is applied through the two condensers to both grids, the positive pulse will not affect the tube which is conducting, since it cannot render it appreciably more conducting. The second tube which

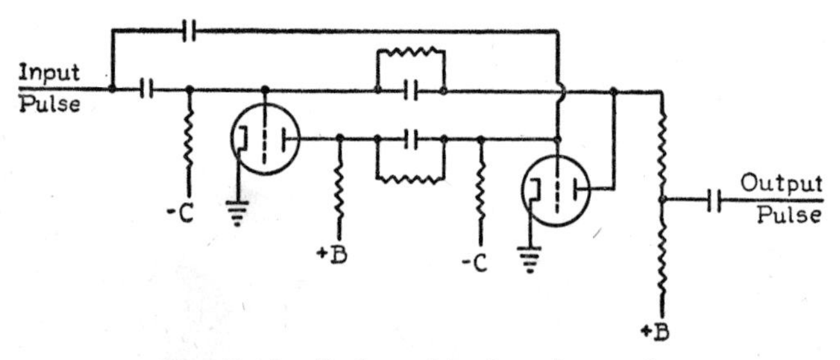

FIG. 7–4A. Eccles and Jordan trigger pair.

is non-conducting, on the other hand, will become conducting and a negative pulse appearing in the plate circuit will be transmitted to the grid of the first tube, causing it to shut off. The circuit will now remain in this new stable condition, which is the inverse of the former state, until the arrival of the next pulse, at which time it will execute one more cycle and return to the initial state. Thus the two tubes alternately conduct and do not conduct. A stage following this unit will therefore receive alternate positive and negative pulses as the tubes fluctuate back and forth between their two states. It is evident that an indefinite number of stages of this type may be built, and many units employing nine stages, in other words, a scale of 512, are in common use at the present time.

In many of the present designs, in-between-stage tubes are used between each trigger pair for the purpose of transmitting pulses of only one sign, and also for the purpose of amplifying the pulse. These interstage tubes may be either triodes or pentodes. Several complete diagrams of multiple scale[L3] counters appear in the literature. A typical scale-of-four is shown complete in Fig. 7–4B.

It is sometimes desirable to know not only when the entire circuit has gone through one cycle, but also how many individual counts have been recorded. Thus, for example, a scale of 32 might have received 25 counts. The output tube would not have received a pulse, but the added 25 counts might be of

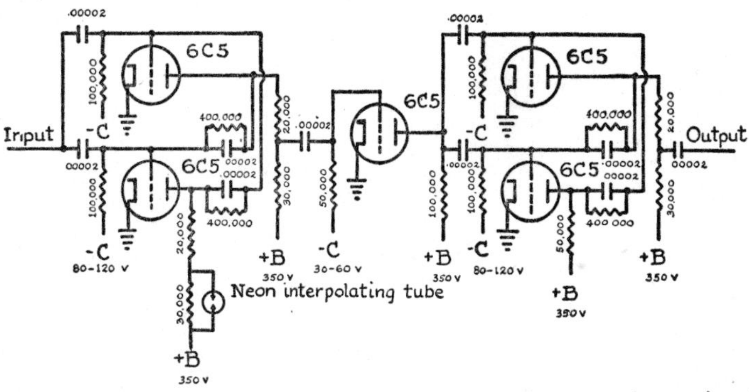

FIG. 7–4B. Triode scale-of-four circuit. Resistances in ohms, capacitances in microfarads. (Ref. L3)

importance in interpreting the results. It is possible by the arrangement of neon lamps across portions of the plate resistor to ascertain how many pulses the entire circuit has responded. One such lamp is put across one resistance in each trigger pair (see Fig. 7–4B), and this light will be either on or off. Thus, for example, if the circuit starts with all lamps off, the first lamp will go on at the appearance of the first pulse. At the appearance of the second pulse, it will go off and the second lamp will go on. At the appearance of the third pulse, the second lamp will remain on and the first will turn on. At the appearance of the fourth pulse, the first and second lamps will go out and the third light goes on, since the impulse has by now reached the third trigger pair. For the fifth pulse the third light remains on and the first light again shows. If we assign the numbers 1, 2, 4, 8, 16, etc., to the neon lamps, one need only add up the numbers corresponding to the lamps which are lit to know the total number of counts which the circuit has recorded.

The resolving time of such trigger circuits is determined by the *RC* time constants of the coupling condensers and resistors. These can readily be made of the order of 0.00005 microfarad and 10^5 ohms, so that time constants of 5 microseconds are

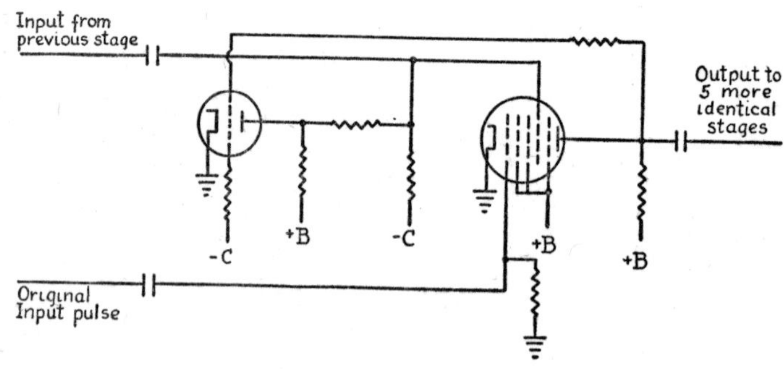

FIG. 7–4C. Scale-of-five ring-scaling circuit.

possible. It is usually not worth making the resolving times much shorter than this figure, owing to the inherent recovery time of the counter, which is already long compared to this. However, a high-speed scaling circuit in conjunction with a high-resolution coincidence circuit is a desirable arrangement for the reduction of accidentals and the accurate measurement of close impulses.

Scales of five or ten are sometimes desired instead of the various powers of two. A diagram of a ring-of-five is shown in Fig. 7–4C. Analysis of the circuit shows that, if all tubes are initially non-conducting, the arrival of a pulse turns the first tube on. Arrival of a second pulse turns the second tube on which in turn feeds back and turns the first tube off. In succession, a third pulse will render the third tube conducting and the second non-conducting. This process continues around all five tubes, the sixth pulse resuming the cycle.

2. Thyratron Scaling Circuits. The properties of thyratrons are particularly suited to the construction of scaling circuits. Such circuits have been devised by Wynn-Williams and others.[W4] A typical circuit of this type is shown in Fig. 7–4D.

The operation of the circuit may be understood by referring to Fig. 7–4D. If one of the tubes is conducting and the other is not conducting, the arrival of a negative pulse on each of the two grids will not affect the system. A negative pulse cannot influence the tube which is not conducting, nor can it

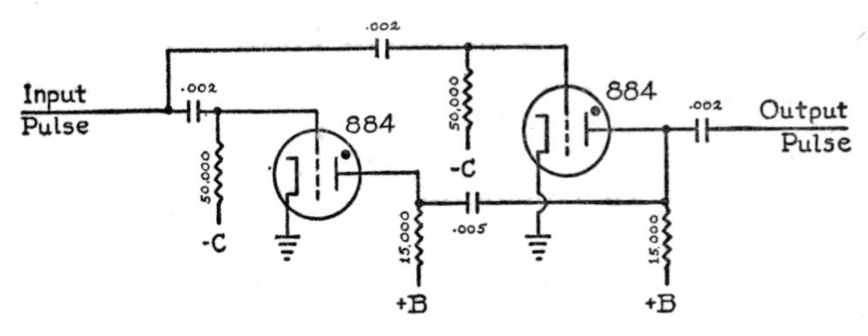

FIG. 7–4D. Thyratron scaling pair. Operates on positive input pulses. Resistances in ohms, capacitances in microfarads.

turn off a thyratron which is conducting since the grid of a gas-filled tube loses control when the tube is glowing. A positive pulse, on the other hand, will cause the non-conducting tube to conduct. When it does so, its plate becomes negative, and the negative pulse is transmitted through the condenser to the other plate, shutting off the first tube by causing its plate potential to be reduced for an instant. The circuit thus locks into the new position with the second tube conducting and the first not conducting. The arrival of another positive pulse will cause this situation to reverse. Thyratron scaling circuits can be employed in multiple units, giving scaling factors of various powers of 2, and many units having a scale of 256 are in successful use. The circuit constants are not at all critical, and the arrangement will work with quite wide variations in the resistance and capacity values.

One fundamental objection to this type of circuit is the inherent de-ionization of the thyratron, which is of the order of 10^{-4} sec. If the time constants of the circuits are reduced much below this figure, the thyratron in question may continue to conduct even though it has received an impulse shutting it off temporarily. The circuit thus becomes unstable and is not suitable for use on extremely fast impulses. Because of the relatively high probability of closely spaced double impulses, this resolving time already presents a serious limitation when random counts at the rate of more than 100 per sec are to be recorded. For faster counting, vacuum tube circuits are to be preferred, although thyratron scales are easier to construct and have less critical dependence on circuit constants.

E. Recording Circuits

The purpose of a recording circuit is to produce an impulse capable of operating some mechanical counting or recording device. Examples of such devices would include a Cenco impulse counter, a telephone message register or any similar arrangement of which many are now in operation. Generally the pulse which is received from the counter is not capable of operating these devices directly. A simple arrangement for so doing, however, may be constructed by using either hard tubes or thyratrons. A typical hard tube circuit, as shown in Fig. 7–5A, uses a multivibrator for recording. In such a circuit the first tube is generally conducting, and the second tube biased to cutoff. The arrival of a negative pulse cuts off the first tube and this in turn produces a positive pulse which causes conduction in the second tube. This second tube is usually a power pentode or triode, in the plate circuit of which is the recording device in question. Usually these recording devices require a pulse of several hundredths of a second duration to operate satisfactorily. Since this is longer than the pulse received from the counter, the necessary time delay may be obtained through the use of the feed-back condenser connecting the plate of the second tube with the grid of the input tube. If the first input tube is a pentode, such as a 6C6 or 6SJ7, a

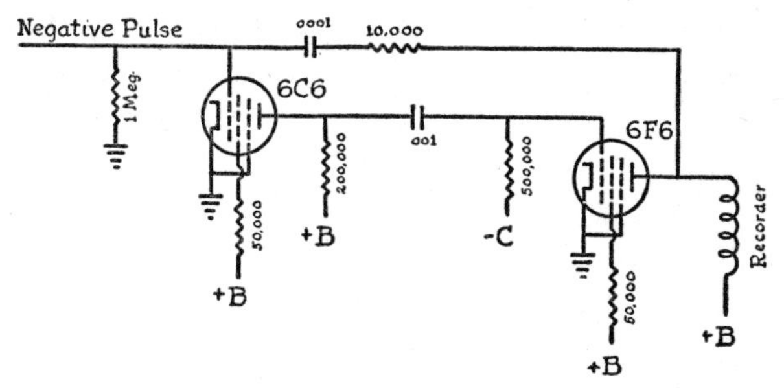

FIG. 7–5A. Multivibrator recorder circuit. Resistances in ohms, capacitances in microfarads.

pulse of a volt or two in amplitude on its grid will produce a swing in its plate of sufficient amplitude to control a power pentode such as a 6F6 or 6L6 satisfactorily.

Thyratron recording circuits are also useful. A typical circuit of this kind is shown in Fig. 7–5B. A thyratron biased to

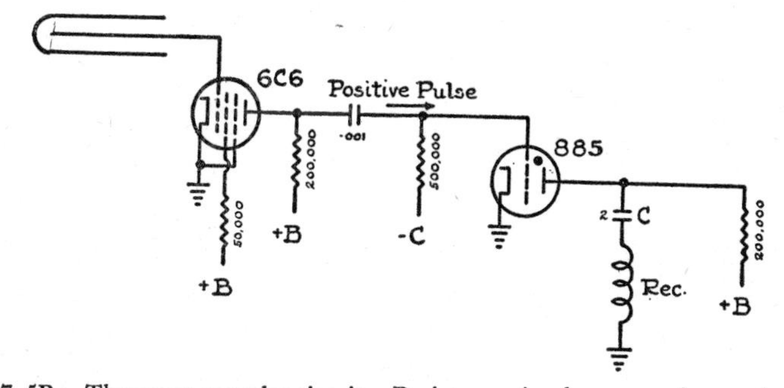

FIG. 7–5B. Thyratron recorder circuit. Resistances in ohms, capacitances in microfarads.

cut-off has the recording device connected through a large condenser to its plate. The plate and one-half of the condenser will be at the potential of the positive terminal of the plate supply as long as the thyratron is non-conducting. If a positive pulse arrives on the grid of the thyratron, it will become conducting. Such a positive pulse could arrive from the plate of a quenching tube in the case of non-selfquenching counters or from the plate of a first stage amplifier following a self-quenching counter. When the thyratron becomes conducting the condenser discharges through it, and the recorder will record a count. The current limiting resistance R_p does not permit enough current to flow, to maintain the thyratron discharge. The discharge therefore ceases and the negative grid resumes control. The charge on the condenser now recovers as current flows through the resistance, and the entire arrangement returns to the state in which it is ready to receive the next impulse. Such a recording arrangement is limited in its speed to the RC time constant of the condenser and current limiting resistance and cannot be reduced too far. If the condenser is made too small, not enough charge will flow to cause the recorder to record unambiguously. On the other hand, if the resistance is made too small, the thyratron will not go out. For fast counting, such a circuit is therefore usually preceded by a scaling circuit.

F. Voltage Supply and Regulating Circuits

Since most laboratories are equipped with a 110 volt, 60 cycle alternating current line, it is customary to operate most of the laboratory equipment on this line. Various types of battery eliminators have consequently been designed. A typical power supply is shown in Fig. 7–6A. It will be seen that this consists of two condensers and one choke. Further condensers and inductances may be added if necessary to smooth out the residual ripple still further. A voltage dividing resistance is shown in the output, and various taps will then provide the potentials required in the several parts of the circuits to be supplied.

The principal difficulties encountered with this type of circuit are (1) that variations in the input voltage are magnified and affect the output voltage, and (2) that the output voltage depends on the load. In order to secure constant output voltages, one of several arrangements are normally employed. If the input frequency is constant, one of the several types of AC voltage regulators may precede the B eliminator. This arrangement is desirable wherever it can be used as it will largely

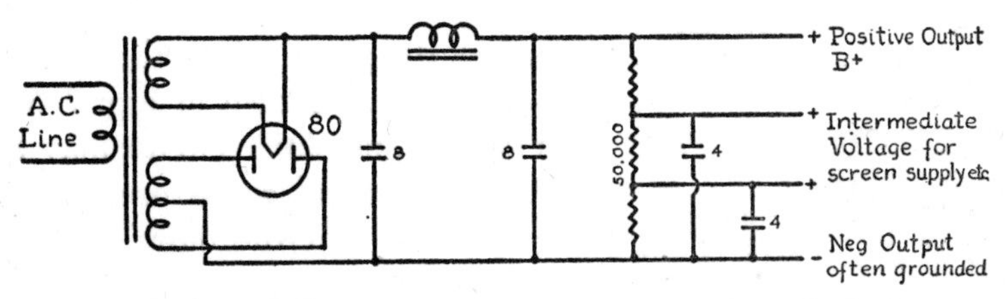

FIG. 7–6A. Ordinary DC power supply or "battery eliminator." Resistances in ohms, capacitances in microfarads.

eliminate fluctuation due to line voltage variations. Such devices are, for example, the Raytheon and the Sola voltage regulators.

Fluctuations due to the changes in the load may be largely eliminated through the use of electronic circuits and devices. One of these is the gas-filled regulator tube. The operation of this device is shown in Fig. 7–6B. Such gas discharge tubes have a flat operating characteristic curve and will in effect maintain a constant voltage across the terminals of the tube for moderate changes in the load. Gas discharge tubes are available for voltages of 75, 90, 105 and 150. These tubes may be used in series, and stabilization may be secured at any voltage such as 165, 180, 195, 450, or other combination sums of these. The tubes in question are the RCA types VR75, 874, VR105 and VR150, respectively. The series resistor must be capable of passing enough current to take care of the load plus the current in the regulating tube, and the power dissipation of this resistor should be calculated.

Electronic voltage regulators are also available and give extremely stable output characteristics. As Hunt and Hickman [H3] have shown, all of these devices may be classified in three categories. The first of these is the transconductance bridge circuit, the second is the amplification factor bridge circuit, and the third is the simple degenerative amplifier. In addition, combination of these three arrangements is possible. Schematic diagrams for the three types of regulators are shown in Fig. 7–6C.

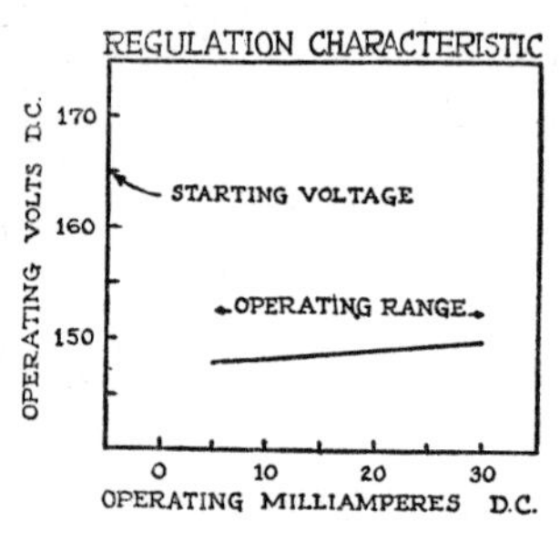

Fig. 7–6B. Characteristic curve of RCA-VR150 voltage-regulating tube. (*R.C.A. Vacuum Handbook*)

In general, no single circuit may be considered as ideal to be used in all circumstances, but the individual arrangements will depend on the problems encountered. Thus, for example, a circuit may be designed to stabilize a high voltage at a low current output, or it may stabilize a comparative low voltage but high current drain. The first and second types of circuits would be quite different. One typical arrangement is shown in Fig. 7–6D. This is a high voltage stabilized supply, capable of producing 10,000 volts for counter potentials. It is important that this voltage should not fluctuate, but at the same time the current capacity required of such a device is extremely small. The circuit shown employs a high gain pentode as the stabilizing tube and is designed to be entirely floating. Either

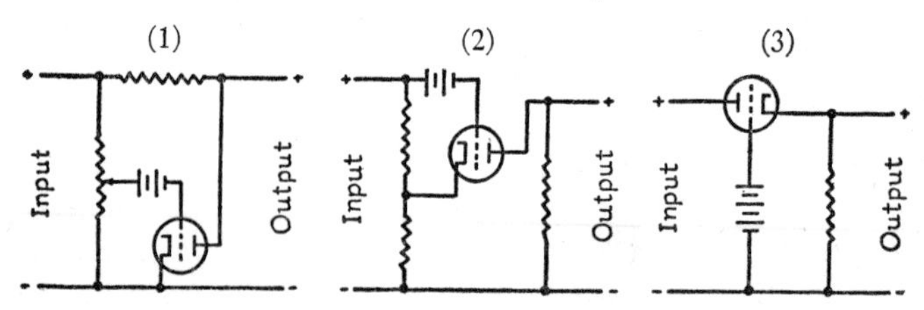

Fig. 7–6C. Schematic voltage-stabilizing circuits. (1) Transconductance bridge. (2) Amplification factor bridge. (3) Degenerative amplifier.

the positive or the negative may be at high potential with respect to ground, although the operation is usually much easier for the high negative and grounded positive. In this case, the cathode of the regulating tube is grounded and the only potential across it is the amount of the regulation. Thus, for example, a 10,000 volt supply can be quite adequately regulated, while the plate of the regulating tube need not be more than

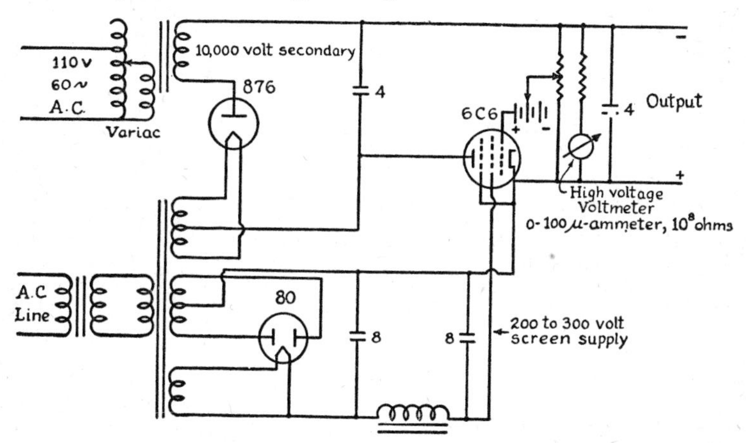

FIG. 7–6D. Complete circuit for producing 10,000 volts DC, regulated, stabilized, adjustable and fully floating. Resistances in ohms, capacitances in microfarads.

a few hundred volts above ground. On the other hand, if the counter is to be operated with the cylinder grounded, the regulating tube will float at a high potential, and the tube as well as its filament and screen voltages must be insulated accordingly. A transformer with a one-to-one ratio, insulated to withstand 10,000 volts, is provided to isolate the regulator system from the 110 volt input line which is customarily grounded on one side.

Another circuit, suitable for regulating a comparative low voltage but high current, is that used in certain commercial regulators. The circuit is shown in Fig. 7–6E. In these devices, a high gain pentode picks up the variations in voltage, its own cathode being held at a constant potential by a gaseous voltage regulating tube. The fluctuations in the potential of its plate are directly connected to the grid of a triode capable of transmitting comparatively large currents. This triode in

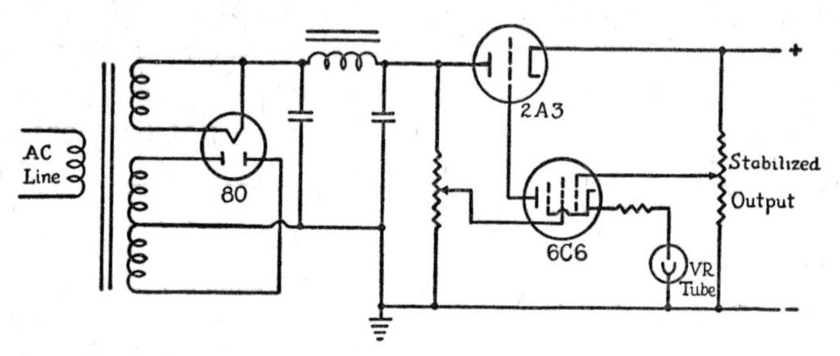

FIG. 7–6E. Voltage-regulating circuit for controlling relatively large currents.

turn regulates the voltage. Thus, for example, if the voltage should increase, the grid of the pentode will become more negative, and the triode in turn will be rendered less conducting. The output will therefore tend to be stable.

In measuring the high potentials for counters, a vacuum tube voltmeter which draws practically no current is desirable.

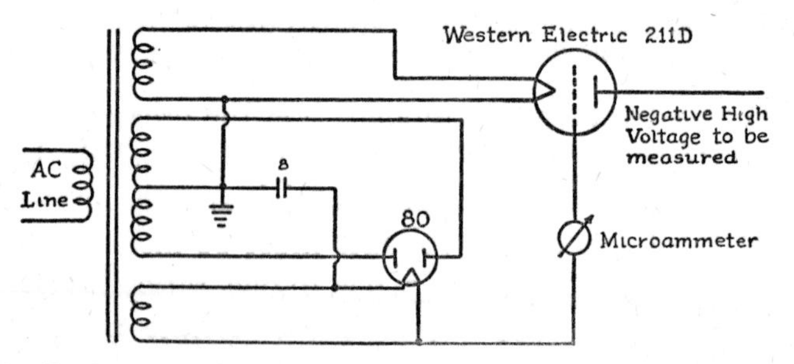

FIG. 7–6F. Vacuum tube voltmeter having high resistance suitable for measuring high negative voltage. The scale can be changed by shunts across the microammeter. This microammeter should also have a variable shunt of 250,000 ohms or so for zero adjustment.

Such a meter, suitable for measuring high negative voltages, is shown in Fig. 7–6F. A triode is operated with its grid positive, and the high negative potential to be measured is applied to its plate.[K12] The application of this voltage produces a field which in turn decreases the grid current. The meter is calibrated by applying known voltages. The grid-current microammeter will read backwards, i.e., it will show a lower current as the voltage applied to the plate increases. A voltmeter of this type can have a resistance of more than 10^9 ohms and will therefore only drain a few microamperes from a several thousand volt supply.

G. Integrating Circuits and Counting Rate Meters

Sometimes it is desirable to employ a device which will show the rate of arrival of pulses. Such a device is called an integrating circuit and, in effect, it adds up all of the pulses which

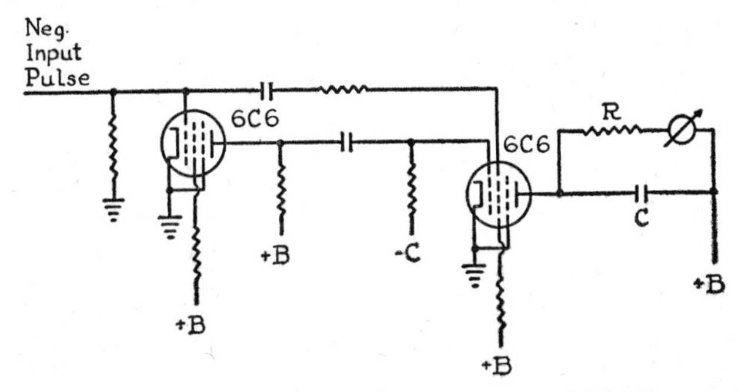

Fig. 7–7A. Integrating circuit or counting-rate meter. Multivibrator for pulse equalizing. Typical *RC* values 100 ohms and 10 microfarads. 0–50 microammeter.

arrive within the time of its time constant. Such integrating circuits may operate by piling charge on a condenser and then measuring the total amount of charge which has arrived.[E2] This can be accomplished by a variety of procedures. For example, pulses may be put onto the condenser from the plate of a vacuum tube, and the rise in potential of the plate of the condenser may be measured by shunting it with a high resistance and microammeter. An arrangement of this sort is shown in Fig. 7–7A.

In the diagram shown, the *RC* time constant of the plate tank circuit is determined by the condenser and by the resistance in series with the microammeter. For example, a 1 microfarad condenser and a 1 megohm resistor will in effect add all the pulses arriving in 1 sec. If the device is recording at the rate of 100 counts per sec, and if each count has a duration of 10^{-4} sec, and further, if the pentode in question conducts 2 milliamperes while the pulse is on, then the total charge arriving on the condenser in 1 sec will be 20 microcoulombs, which

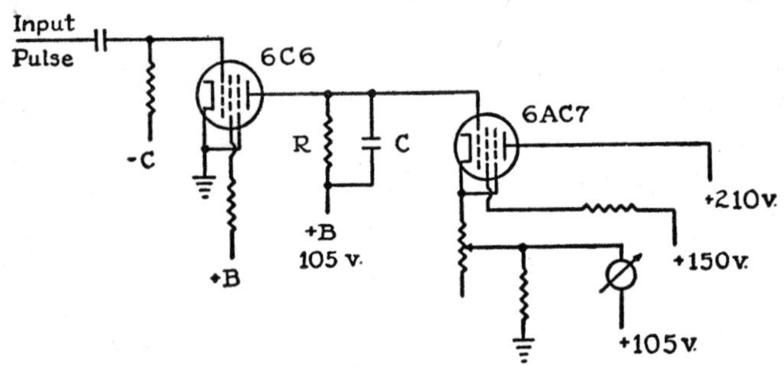

FIG. 7–7B. Vacuum tube voltmeter type of integrating circuit. Second tube acts as voltmeter measuring potentials in *RC* tank circuit.

in turn will produce a rise in potential of the plate of the condenser of 20 volts. A current of 20 microamperes will flow through the one megohm resistor and this current may be read with ease on a 0–50 microammeter.

Alternatively, the rise in potential of the condenser may be measured on a vacuum tube voltmeter. A typical circuit of this type is shown in Fig. 7–7B. Here the first tube receives and amplifies the pulses which are stored on the condenser in the plate tank circuit. The rise in potential of this condenser is then directly communicated to the grid of the second tube, the plate current of which indicates its grid voltage, serving thus as a vacuum tube voltmeter. The plate current of the final tube may be calibrated directly in counts per minute. The scale may be varied by altering the values of the *RC* time constant of the first grid cuircuit.

The operation of any device which depends on adding pulses presupposes that the pulses are all of the same size. It is therefore in general necessary to precede the integrating tube by a multivibrator pulse-equalizing stage. Such a multivibrator may use the integrating tube as one component, as is shown in Fig. 7–7A. The magnitude of the reading of the microammeter will depend on the amplitude and breadth of the pulse. The scale of the instrument may therefore be changed by altering the coupling condenser connecting the plate of the first tube with the control grid of the integrating tube. Similarly the grid resistor and plate resistor connected to this condenser will also determine the magnitude of the reading of the microammeter. The values in question are therefore adjusted for convenience, and a range switch may be included to select the values appropriate to any particular problem.

H. Pulse Amplifiers

The pulse amplifiers used in connection with Geiger and proportional counters are generally resistance-capacity coupled amplifiers with definite frequency characteristics. The linearity of their response may vary greatly. Those instruments in which the amplification is constant, for input pulse heights in a certain range, are spoken of as "linear amplifiers." In other amplifiers the condition of linearity is not met, and the amount of amplification varies with the pulse height. Such non-linear amplifiers are quite common and indeed, if a certain range of pulse sizes is exceeded, all amplifiers will have non-linear characteristics. The linear amplifier is therefore merely a special case of the pulse amplifier, and represents one in which the amplification is a constant for a range of pulse heights. Most amplifiers will show a saturation effect, the output pulse being limited to a certain size.

The gain which an amplifier may have can vary over wide limits. It is possible to construct amplifiers having little or no gain and others having a gain of 10^6 or more. Special precautions must be observed in constructing any high gain amplifier. Shielding must be good. It is usually necessary to screen each individual stage from every other stage. The input stage in particular has to be thoroughly shielded. This is ordinarily accomplished by building the stage in question inside a metal box. All leads connecting any one stage with other stages or supplying it with power must pass through shielded conductors. No portion of any stage can be permitted to "look" out into the room, since if a straight line can be drawn between any portion of the amplifier and any portion of the 60 cycle lighting circuit, excessive pickup will result. This is the familiar principle of electrostatic shielding. Multiple grounds should also be avoided. A grounded cable can be provided in the amplifier to which all grounded leads are attached. This grounded cable should be connected to the metal box at only one point, and the metal box should not be used as a conductor or as part of the circuit.

The limits of frequency response of an amplifier are determined by the resistance-capacity coupling network. A simple illustration is given below. We will assume that it is desired to amplify pulses from a Geiger counter or proportional counter. These pulses have the characteristics which we have previously described, namely, a fast break and a longer recovery. The break takes place in an interval of the order of a microsecond and the recovery in an interval about 100 times as long. We also desire that this amplifier should not respond to the 60 cycle AC line frequency. It is therefore desirable that the amplifier should operate only in the range between 10^6 and 10^3 cycles per sec. The upper limit insures that the fast break of the counter will be faithfully followed, and the lower limit assures that the recovery will be followed but the 60 cycle AC pickup will be negligible.

Consider a coupling circuit, such as shown in Fig. 7–8A, consisting of a condenser and two resistances. Let a pulse, i.e., a change of voltage dV/dt, of longer duration than the *RC* time of the circuit, be fed into the circuit. Then the condenser will discharge through the resistance as fast as the charge arrives, and the grid of the second tube will not receive an appreciable signal. The circuit therefore has a low frequency limit determined by its *RC* time constant. If we desire a long time limit or low frequency limit of the order of 10^{-3} sec, we might use a resistance of 10^5 ohms and a coupling condenser of 0.01 microfarad.

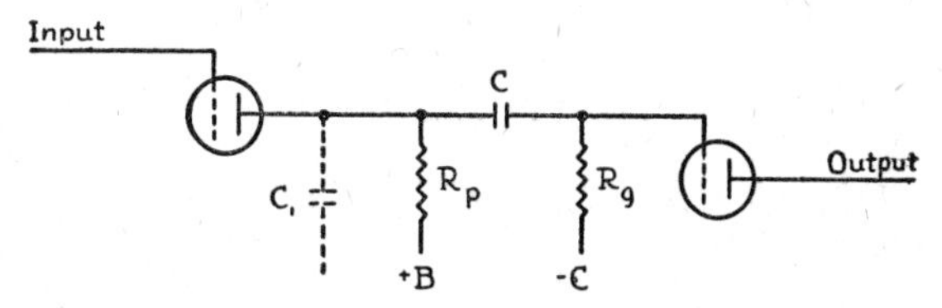

FIG. 7–8A. Resistance-capacity interstage coupling.

The high frequency limit of the circuit is usually determined by the vacuum tube employed. Each vacuum tube has a certain internal capacity between the grid and cathode and, if a pulse of extremely short duration is fed into it, most of the pulse will be by-passed to ground through the internal capacity, and also through the distributed capacity of the system. Since the internal capacity of most vacuum tubes is of the order of a few micromicrofarads, it follows that with the same resistance of 10^5 ohms the high frequency limit will be a few megacycles. A high frequency cutoff can also be arranged by connecting a small condenser across the plate resistor, as indicated in the dotted portion of Fig. 7–8A. This condenser and the plate resistor will determine an *RC* time, and any pulse shorter than this will pass through the condenser to ground. This arrangement is used whenever it is desired to eliminate the response to high frequencies. The two condensers C and C_1 determine the low and high frequency values of the coupling system. It is evident that they may be adjusted to any desired value. The figures given are those appropriate to Geiger counters.

If an ionization chamber is to be used, the collection time of the ions should be determined and the time constant of the resulting pulse may be computed. The *RC* values of the circuit should then be chosen so that the pulse in question will be passed but the sensitivity of the amplifier in other frequency ranges, and consequently its sensitivity to noise and disturbances, is minimized. In most ionization chambers the collection time is considerably longer than in counters. Therefore it

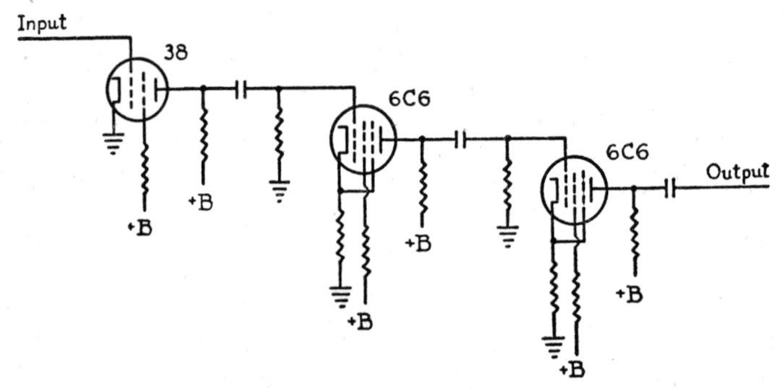

FIG. 7–8B. Extra-linear amplifier.

is desirable to use an amplifying circuit employing a frequency characteristic which brackets the appropriate time constant of the collecting chamber.

A typical pulse amplifier using coupling of the type described is shown in Fig. 7–8B. Many circuits of this type have been described in the literature, such as those designed by Roberts [R7] and others. These amplifiers are essentially non-linear in their response and merely serve to amplify the pulse produced by the counter.

In other applications it is desirable to know the size of the pulse, and for this the linear amplifier is used. A diagram of the linear amplifier is shown in Fig. 7–8C. Such amplifiers have been designed by Lewis [L4] and many others. The design of high gain linear amplifiers is a specialized subject and one fraught with pitfalls for the unwary. Design should not be undertaken by the inexperienced, except under competent direction. The literature on the subject is extensive and worth considerable study. A complete discussion of linear amplifiers would be out of place in this volume. However, a few of the salient considerations which apply, not only to linear amplifiers but to other types of amplifiers as well, will be discussed.

One of the problems encountered in high gain amplifiers is noise. Noise ultimately determines the maximum gain which

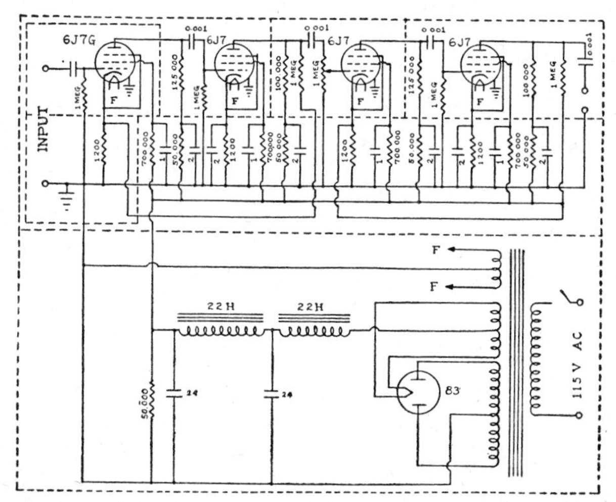

Fig. 7–8C. Four stage degenerative linear amplifier. Resistances in ohms, capacitances in microfarads. (Petruskas and Van Atta, *Rev. Sci. Inst.* **11**, 104 (1940))

may be obtained from the amplifier. Noise has many origins, and the recognition of each as well as its remedy depends on its nature. The various types of noise may be classified as (a) noise due to pickup, (b) noise due to voltage fluctuations and disturbances in the batteries, (c) noise due to oscillations and feedback, (d) shot effect in vacuum tubes, (e) temperature noises in resistors, and (f) noise produced by thermal agitation in the input circuit.

Noise due to pickup is minimized by (a) limiting the frequency response of the amplifier to the range bracketing the pulses to be detected and (b) adequate shielding. Noise due to voltage fluctuations is minimized by using only batteries and not power supplies operated from the AC line. The batteries should be new and of high current capacity compared to the drain expected from them. Storage batteries should be freshly charged. All batteries should be kept in metal-lined boxes and connected to the circuit through shielded conductors. High capacity condensers to ground at various points in the circuit help to by-pass undesirable noises. Feed-back between stages should be minimized by proper shielding. Wire-wound resistances should be used instead of carbon or "metallized" types. Thin films of metal or carbon frequently produce electrical noise. Care should be taken with all contacts to insure that there is ample pressure, since loose contacts are noisy. Wherever possible the contacts should be carefully soldered. This statement applies even to the connections to the pins of the first stage vacuum tubes in the circuit, as contacts in ordinary tube sockets may be noisy. Indeed it is often advisable to dispense with the socket and solder directly to the tube prongs.

The shot effect in vacuum tubes, due to the finite value of the charge of the electron, may be identified by the fact that it increases with the plate current of the first tube. The plate current should therefore be kept as low as possible. It is customary to operate the tube at reduced potentials to achieve this result. Thus, for example, an RCA type 38, rated for 6.3 volt heater and 180 volts plate potential in normal operation, may be operated on 4 volts heater supply and 22½ volts screen, 45 volts plate, with improved performance as regards noise.

In order to provide a high input impedance, the first tube must have a high grid resistance. In addition, since it is operated with a high resistance grid resistor or none at all, the tube must "float" in the operating range, i.e., when nothing at all is connected to the grid, the plate current must be part way between zero and maximum value. Then, if the potential of the grid is slightly altered, the plate current will change. The grid current must be extremely low. Most vacuum tubes "float" either cut off or passing full plate current. In these circumstances the tube is insensitive to minor changes in the grid potential. Of the inexpensive receiving tubes currently available, the RCA type 38 is one of the few that meets these requirements. Selected tubes may have grid resistances of 10^9 to 10^{11} ohms. In certain cases the RCA type 89 may be used. However, for precision work, and for detection of the smallest possible voltage fluctuations, the General Electric Pliotron type FP54 is suitable. This tube has a grid resistance of around 10^{14} to 10^{15} ohms, if operated with 4 volts screen and 6 volts plate potential.

Noise produced by thermal agitation in the input will be independent of the plate current of the first tube. It is generally of a low frequency character and may be minimized by cutting out all frequencies lower than 0.1 sec by the filter characteristics or *RC* values of the coupling circuits.

In designing a good linear amplifier, it is frequently useful to employ degenerative feed-back. In this arrangement a portion of the output signal is fed back from the plate to the grid, but its phase is reversed. This results in decreasing the amplitude of the output signal and would at first sight appear to nullify the purpose of the amplifier. However, negative feed-back greatly improves the frequency characteristics of the amplifier, increases its stability, may reduce noise, reduces dependence of gain on battery voltages, and helps to make the gain independent of the load. If B is the gain of the amplifier without feed-back, and a fraction b of the output signal is fed back into the input, then it can be shown that the gain with the feed-back, B_f, is given by

$$B_f = B/(1 - Bb)$$

The advantages in frequency response and stability are achieved at the expense of a loss of amplification. Since, with modern vacuum tubes it is comparatively easy to add a stage or two of amplification to make up for the gain lost through the feed-back, many modern amplifiers employ this principle because of the improvement in performance thus secured.

I. Miscellaneous Circuits

A wide variety of other circuits, designed to perform specialized functions, has also been developed during the past few years. We shall describe briefly a few of the more useful of these.

A pulse generator, capable of producing pulses with adjustable amplitude, with adjustable frequency, and with adjustable

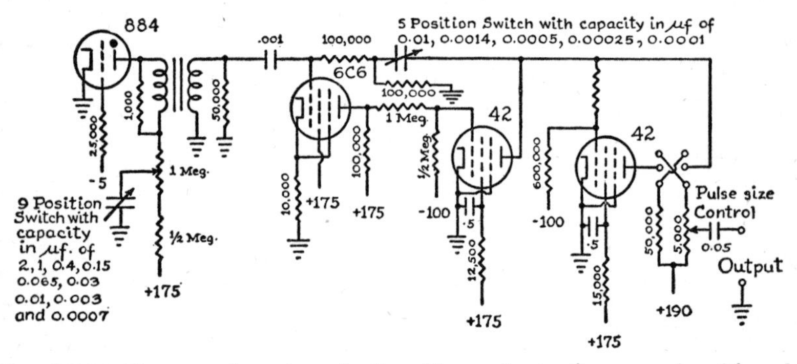

Fig. 7–9A. Generator for pulses of adjustable amplitude, frequency, breadth and sign. Potentials in volts, resistances in ohms, condensers in microfarads.

pulse breadth, was built by Manning and Young.[M6] Such a device is useful in testing scaling circuits and recording equipment. The diagram of this circuit is given in Fig. 7–9A. It will be seen that the device is essentially a thyratron relaxation oscillator, the frequency of which is controlled by the variable resistance and capacity R and C. The second variable condenser C_2 controls the pulse breadth, and the second variable resistor R_2 controls pulse height. The instrument may be calibrated by beating against a standard oscillator.

A pulse equalizing and sharpening circuit has been described by Huntoon and Strohmeyer.[H4] Such a circuit, Fig. 7–9B, is often used to precede a high speed scaling circuit or an integrating circuit, since the counter pulses may be non-uniform. A pulse of either sign may be fed into the circuit, the grid bias being altered accordingly, and pulses of either sign may be obtained from its output. The circuit is similar to a stage of a scaling (trigger) circuit, except that the tubes are unequally

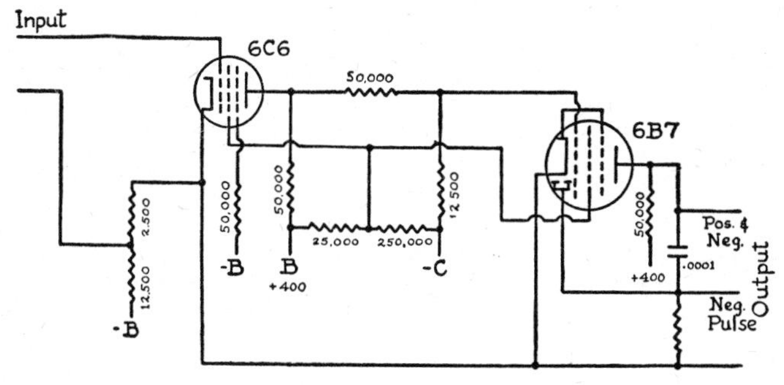

Fig. 7–9B. Pulse equalizing and sharpening circuit. Resistances in ohms, capacitances in microfarads. (Ref. H4)

biased and there is only one stable operating state instead of two.

An interval measuring circuit has been described by Weisz.[W5] This circuit, Fig. 7–9C(1), permits the measurement of the interval between pulses and operates by making use of the charging time of a condenser. Weisz also describes a pulse generator producing a pair of pulses with known and adjustable spacing. Such a generator is helpful in calibrating and testing scaling circuits. Fig. 7–9C(2) shows such a circuit, which again makes use of the charging time of a condenser.

Electronic high voltage supplies are often used in counter problems to provide the counter potential. Several such circuits have been designed, by Huntoon, Barry, Neher and others.[H5, B7, N3] All essentially make use of the relation

$$V = L\,di/dt$$

where the voltage V is determined by the time rate of variation of the current i in a circuit with inductance L. If we apply

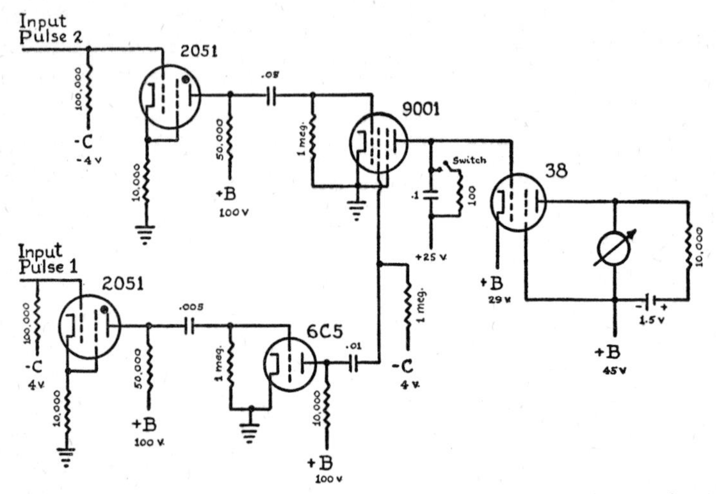

Fig. 7–9C(1). Circuit for measuring interval between pulses. Resistances in ohms, capacitances in microfarads. (Ref. W5)

a rapidly varying current to an inductance, a voltage will be generated which can be rectified and used to charge a condenser. For example, in Fig. 7–9D, the triode-pentode pair con-

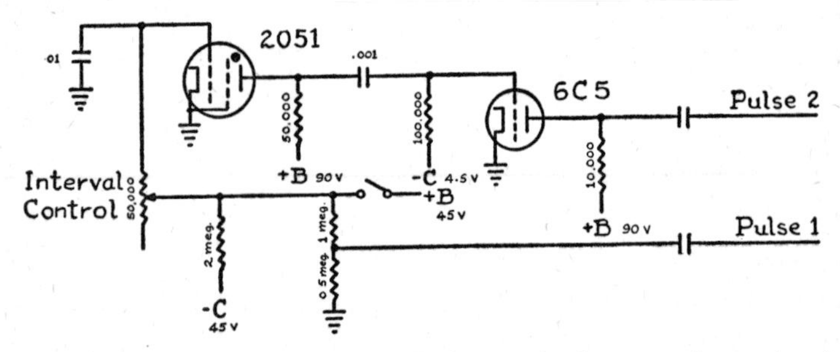

Fig. 7–9C(2). Double pulse generator. Resistances in ohms, capacitances in microfarads. (Ref. W5)

nected as a multivibrator produces the varying current which is applied to the inductance L, and the resulting emf is then rectified by the diode. The condenser C becomes charged to a voltage determined by the inductance L and resistors and condensers of the multivibrator circuit. A multivibrator is used rather than a sinusoidal oscillator, for it produces more nearly "square" waves with a steep wave-front. This steep front gives a rapid variation of current, as its slope di/dt is large. Such voltage supplies can produce over 2000 volts, using ordinary triodes and about 45 to 90 volts plate potential, and are

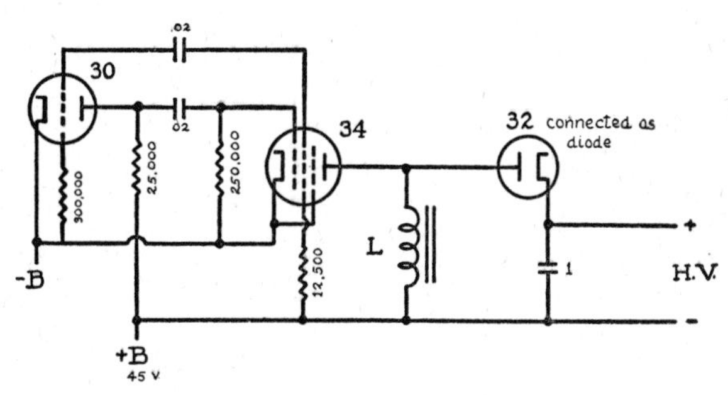

FIG. 7–9D. Electronic high voltage generator. Resistances in ohms, capacitances in microfarads. (Ref. H5)

useful when AC is not available or when high voltage batteries would be inconvenient.

A specialized type of coincidence measuring circuit has been developed by Ramsey [R8] for use in connection with multiple counters when, for example, it is desired that an output pulse shall occur whenever any three out of a bank of ten counters discharge simultaneously. Ramsey's circuit makes use of the fact that the pulses of identical Geiger counters are all of a constant size. Suppose the several counters all have their central wires connected together (Fig. 7–9E). The wires are connected to the grid of a pentode biased to a positive potential. Any negative pulse greater than some assignable value will cause the tube to cut off, or to become non-conducting. However, any pulse smaller than this will not affect the conductivity of the tube. Let us say it requires −6 volts to render the tube non-conducting, and let the grid potential be 0. Further, let us adjust the overvoltage on the counters so that each time a counter counts a 2 volt pulse appears on the com-

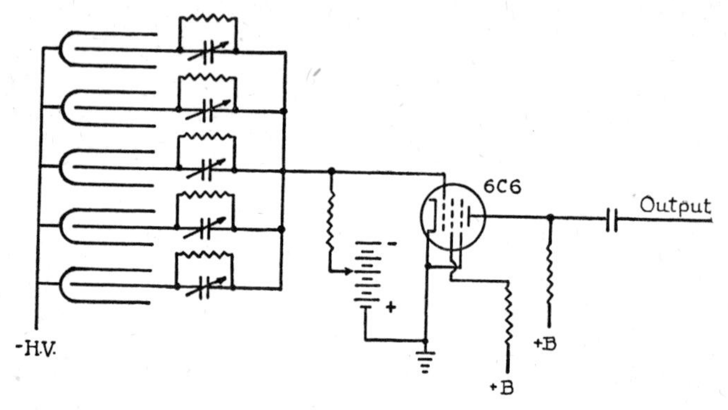

Fig. 7–9E. Circuit to determine when any assignable number of counters discharge coincidentally. The pulses are additive, and the number is controlled by the grid bias.

mon central wire system. Then a coincidence due to any three will cause the plate current in the pentode to cease, thus producing a pulse. Should fourfold coincidences be required, the pentode grid potential is set at $+2$ volts; while for double coincidences, we set it at -2 volts. Any number of coincidences may thus be selected and determined. Resistance-quenched

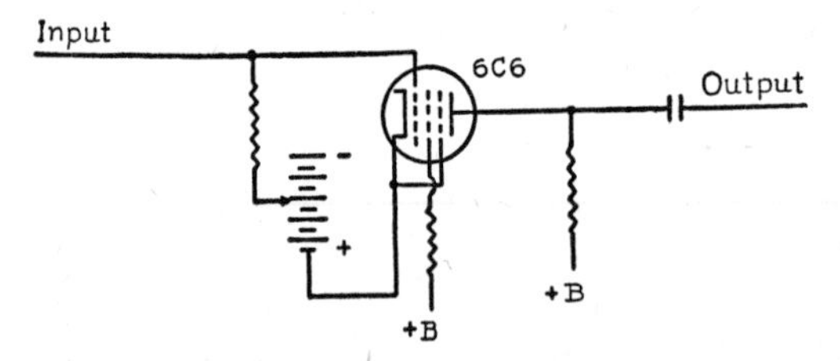

Fig. 7–9F. Discriminator. A tube with an adjustable grid bias, which will pass all pulses greater than a certain size, determined by the grid bias, and which rejects smaller pulses.

counters are assumed in the diagram. The variable condensers allow accurate balancing to make up for minor variations and permit all counters to be adjusted so as to give pulses of exactly the same size. Either selfquenching or non-selfquenching counters may be used. The resistance R connected across the condenser is either high or low, accordingly.

Discriminator circuits are frequently useful. These circuits record only pulses greater than a certain size. This goal can be accomplished in a variety of ways,[L4] usually by adjusting the grid bias of a tube to a certain value. This bias must be overcome before the tube becomes operative. The tube may be a vacuum tube or a thyratron (Fig. 7–9F). Such circuits are used, for example, to separate large pulses, produced in a proportional counter due to neutrons, from a background of smaller pulses due to gamma rays. If the counter wires are tied together, this circuit can determine the distribution of double, triple, quadruple and greater-fold discharges.

Conclusion. It would be possible to describe an almost indefinite number of auxiliary electronic circuits. Discussion has been confined to those which in the author's opinion are most generally useful. A few more are appended as references. This list is not complete, and the reader will find many more in the literature. The subject is expanding rapidly and, as new tubes become available, the reader may enjoy working out new modifications. Detailed discussions of circuits may be found in the standard texts on electronics.

"Interval Selector." A. Roberts, *R.S.I.* **12,** 71 (1941)
"Ionization Chamber Circuit." S. W. Barnes, *R.S.I.* **10,** 1 (1939)
"Linear Amplifier." C. E. Wynn-Williams and F. A. B. Ward, *P.R.S.* **131,** 391 (1931)
R. C. Waddell, *R.S.I.* **10,** 311 (1939)
A. A. Petruskas and C. A. Van Atta, *R.S.I.* **11,** 103 (1940)
G. P. Harnwell and L. N. Ridenour, *R.S.I.* **11,** 346 (1940)
"D.C. Amplifiers." D. B. Pennick, *Rev. Sci. Inst.* **6,** 117 (1935); A. W. Vance, *Rev. Sci. Inst.* **7,** 490 (1936)
"Triode Scaler." D. DeVault, *R.S.I.* **12,** 83 (1941)

"Double Pulse Generator." A. Roberts, *R.S.I.* **10,** 316 (1939)
"Pulse Amplitude Selector." A. Roberts, *R.S.I.* **11,** 44 (1940)
"Electron Multiplier as Counter." Z. Bay, *R.S.I.* **12,** 127 (1941)
"Resolving Time Measurement." Y. Beers, *R.S.I.* **13,** 72 (1942)

The following texts on electronics contain much useful material on circuits and circuit analysis methods:

Theory and Application of Electron Tubes, H. S. Reich, McGraw-Hill (1939)
Electronics, J. Millman and S. Seely, McGraw-Hill (1941)

The following books are often found useful in connection with counter problems:

Electrical Phenomena in Gases, K. K. Darrow, Williams & Wilkins (1932)
Radiations from Radioactive Substances, E. Rutherford, J. Chadwick and C. D. Ellis, Cambridge (1930)
Procedures in Experimental Physics, J. Strong, Prentice-Hall (1938)
Electrical Counting, W. B. Lewis, Cambridge (1942)
Fundamental Processes of Electrical Discharges in Gases, L. Loeb, Wiley (1938)

Commercial references: *

Counters and circuits are manufactured commercially by:
Technical Associates, Glendale 4, Cal.
Cyclotron Specialties Co., Moraga, Cal.
Herbach & Rademan, Market St., Philadelphia, Pa.

* At the suggestion of colleagues, a list of a few commercial organizations supplying equipment useful in constructing and operating counters is included. Omission of the names of some manufacturers may be attributed to inadvertence and not to any implication that their products are, in the author's opinion, inferior.

Voltage regulators for stabilizing AC are made by:
Raytheon Mfg. Co., Waltham, Mass.
Sola Electric Co., Chicago, Ill.
Copper tubes for counter cylinders are made by:
Improved Seamless Wire Co., 775 Eddy St., Providence, R. I.
Glass blowing on counters is done by:
Eck & Krebs, 131 West 24th St., New York City, N. Y.
Glass for counters is manufactured by:
Corning Glass Works, Corning, N. Y.
Metal-to-glass seals are made by:
Stupakoff Laboratories, Pittsburgh, Pa.
Electronic voltage stabilizers are made by:
RCA Manufacturing Co.
Harvey Radio Lab., 444 Concord Ave., Cambridge 38, Mass.

REFERENCES

B1 W. Bothe and H. Kolhorster, *Zeits. f. Phys.* **56,** 571 (1929)
B2 H. A. Bethe, *Revs. Mod. Phys.* **9,** 69 (1937)
B3 S. C. Brown, *Phys. Rev.* **62,** 244 (1942)
B4 S. C. Brown, L. A. Elliott and R. D. Evans, *Rev. Sci. Inst.* **13,** 147 (1942)
B5 H. Bateman, *Phil. Mag.* **20,** 704 (1910)
B6 G. Brubaker and E. Pollard, *Rev. Sci. Inst.* **8,** 254 (1937)
B7 J. G. Barry, *Rev. Sci. Inst.* **12,** 136 (1941)

C1 A. H. Compton, E. O. Wollan and R. D. Bennett, *Rev. Sci. Inst.* **5,** 415 (1934)
C2 K. T. Compton and I. Langmuir, *Revs. Mod. Phys.* **2,** 191 (1930)
C3 M. Cosyns, *Bull. Tech. Ing. Ecole Polytech. Brux.* (1936)
C4 D. B. Cowie, *Phys. Rev.* **48,** 883 (1935)
C5 L. F. Curtiss, *Bur. of Stds. J. of Res.* **10,** 229 (1932)

D1 K. K. Darrow, *Electrical Phenomena in Gases*, Williams and Wilkins (1932)
D2 W. E. Danforth, *Phys. Rev.* **46,** 1026 (1934)
D3 W. E. Danforth and W. E. Ramsey, *Phys. Rev.* **49,** 854 (1936)

E1 W. H. Eccles and F. W. Jordan, *Radio Rev.* **1,** 143 (1919)
E2 R. D. Evans and R. E. Meagher, *Rev. Sci. Inst.* **10,** 339 (1939)

G1 H. Geiger, *Verh. d. D. Phys. Ges.* **15,** 534 (1913); *Phys. Zeits* **14,** 1129 (1913)
G2 H. Geiger and E. Rutherford, *Phil. Mag.* **24,** 618 (1912)
G3 H. Geiger and W. Muller, *Phys. Zeits.* **29,** 839 (1928); **30,** 489 (1929)
G4 H. Geiger and O. Klemperer, *Zeits. f. Phys.* **49,** 753 (1928)
G5 K. Greisen and N. Nereson, *Phys. Rev.* **62,** 326 (1942)
G6 G. Glockler, Proc. *Nat. Acad. Sci.* **11,** 74 (1925)
G7 I. A. Getting, *Phys. Rev.* **53,** 103 (1938)

H1 V. F. Hess and R. W. Lawson, *Wiener Ber.* **127,** 599 (1918)
H2 G. Herzog, *Rev. Sci. Inst.* **11,** 84 (1940)

H3 F. V. Hunt and R. W. Hickman, *Rev. Sci. Inst.* **10**, 6 (1939)
H4 R. D. Huntoon and L. J. Strohmeyer, *Rev. Sci. Inst.* **12**, 35 (1941)
H5 R. D. Huntoon, *Rev. Sci. Inst.* **10**, 176 (1939)
H6 W. E. Hazen, *Phys. Rev.* **63**, 107 (1943)

J1 T. H. Johnson, *Rev. Sci. Inst.* **9**, 218 (1938)
J2 T. H. Johnson and S. A. Korff, *Terr. Mag. & Atm. Elec.* **44**, 23 (1939)

K1 C. Kenty, *Phys. Rev.* **32**, 624 (1928)
K2 W. R. Kanne and J. A. Bearden, *Phys. Rev.* **50**, 935 (1936)
K3 S. A. Korff and W. E. Danforth, *Phys. Rev.* **55**, 980 (1939)
K4 S. A. Korff, *Revs. Mod. Phys.* **14**, 1 (1942)
K5 S. A. Korff and E. T. Clarke, *Phys. Rev.* **61**, 422 (1942)
K6 S. A. Korff and W. E. Danforth, *J. Franklin Inst.* **228**, 159 (1939)
K7 S. A. Korff and R. D. Present, *Phys. Rev.* **65**, 274 (1944)
K8 H. Kallman and B. Rosen, *Ziets. f. Phys.* **61**, 61 (1930)
K9 S. A. Korff, W. Spatz and N. Hilberry, *Rev. Sci. Inst.* **13**, 127 (1942)
K10 S. A. Korff, *Proc. Am. Philos. Soc.* **84**, 589 (1941)
K11 S. A. Korff and W. E. Ramsey, *Rev. Sci. Inst.* **11**, 267 (1940); *Phys. Rev.* **68**, 53 (1945)
K12 M. Kupferberg, *Rev. Sci. Inst.* **14**, 254 (1943)

L1 L. B. Loeb, *Fundamental Processes of Electrical Discharges in Gases*, Wiley (1939)
L2 G. L. Locher, *Phys. Rev.* **55**, 675A (1939)
L3 H. Lifschutz and J. L. Lawson, *Rev. Sci. Inst.* **9**, 83 (1938); **10**, 21 (1939)
L4 W. B. Lewis, *Electrical Counting*, Cambridge, 1942
L5 W. F. Libby, *Phys. Rev.* **55**, 245 (1939)

M1 C. G. and D. D. Montgomery, *J. Franklin Inst.* **231**, 447 (1941)
M2 R. A. Millikan and H. V. Neher, *Phys. Rev.* **50**, 15 (1936)
M3 C. G. and D. D. Montgomery, *Phys. Rev.* **57**, 1030 (1940)
M4 H. S. W. Massey, *Proc. Camb. Phil. Soc.* **26**, 386 (1930)
M5 C. G. and D. D. Montgomery, *Rev. Sci. Inst.* **11**, 237 (1940)
M6 H. P. Manning and V. J. Young, *Rev. Sci. Inst.* **13**, 234 (1942)

N1 H. V. Neher and W. H. Pickering, *Phys. Rev.* **53,** 316 (1938)
N2 H. V. Neher and W. W. Harper, *Phys. Rev.* **49,** 940 (1936)
N3 H. V. Neher and W. H. Pickering, *Rev. Sci. Inst.* **12,** 140 (1941)

O1 M. L. E. Oliphant and P. B. Moon, *Proc. Roy. Soc. A* **127,** 388 (1930)

R1 E. Rutherford and H. Geiger, *Proc. Roy. Soc. A* **81,** 141 (1908)
R2 B. Rossi, N. Cimento **8,** 49 and 85 (1931); *Zeits. f. Phys.* **68,** 64 (1931); *Proc. Lond. Conf. Nuc. Phys.* (1934); *Acad. Lencei Atti* **13,** 47 and 600 (1931)
R3 M. E. Rose and S. A. Korff, *Phys. Rev.* **59,** 850 (1941)
R4 M. E. Rose and W. E. Ramsey, *Phys. Rev.* **61,** 198 (1942)
R5 W. E. Ramsey, *Phys. Rev.* **57,** 1022 and 1061 (1940)
R6 G. K. Rollefson and M. Burton, *Photochemistry*, Prentice-Hall (1939)
R7 R. B. Roberts, *Rev. Sci. Inst.* **9,** 98 (1938)
R8 W. E. Ramsey, *Phys. Rev.* **57,** 1061 (1940)

S1 W. D. B. Spatz, *Phys. Rev.* **64,** 236 (1943)
S2 W. F. G. Swann, *J. Franklin Inst.* **216,** 559 (1933); **230,** 281 (1940)
S3 H. G. Stever, *Phys. Rev.* **61,** 38 (1942)
S4 J. A. Simpson, *Phys. Rev.* **662,** 39 (1944)
S5 J. A. Simpson, *Rev. Sci. Inst.* **15,** 119 (1944)
S6 W. D. B. Spatz, Private communication.
S7 J. A. Simpson, Private communication.
S8 H. K. Skramstad and D. H. Loughridge, *Phys. Rev.* **50,** 677 (1936)
S9 L. I. Schiff and R. D. Evans, *Rev. Sci. Inst.* **7,** 456 (1936)

T1 M. A. Tuve, *Phys. Rev.* **35,** 651 (1930)
T2 A. Trost, *Zeits. f. Phys.* **105,** 399 (1937)

W1 S. Werner, *Zeits. f. Phys.* **90,** 384 (1934); **92,** 705 (1934)
W2 M. H. Wilkening and W. R. Kanne, *Phys. Rev.* **62,** 534 (1942)
W3 C. E. Wynn-Williams, *Brit. Pat.* No. 421341
W4 C. E. Wynn-Williams, *Proc. Roy. Soc. A* **136,** 312 (1932)
W5 P. Weisz, *Electronics* **17,** 108 (1944)

Additional Bibliography on Counters Not Specifically Referred to in the Text

J. S. Allan and T. U. Alvarez, *Rev. Sci. Inst.* **6,** 329 (1936)
H. Aoki, A. Narimatu and M. Scotani, *Proc. Phys-Math. Soc.* Japan **22,** 746–749 (1940)
E. V. Appleton, K. G. Emeleus and M. A. Barnett, *Proc. Camb. Phys. Soc.*
Y. Beers, *Rev. Sci. Inst.* **13,** 72 (1942)
R. D. Bennett, J. C. Stearns and W. P. Overbeck, *Rev. Sci. Inst.* **4,** 387 (1933)
G. Bernadini, D. Bocciarelli and F. Oppenheimer, *Rev. Sci. Inst.* **7,** 382 (1936)
W. Bothe, *Zeits. f. Phys.* **59,** 1 (1929)
W. C. Bosch, *Rev. Sci. Inst.* **9,** 308 (1938)
F. Burger-Scheidlin, Ann. Physik **12,** 283–304 (1932)
A. W. Coven, *Rev. Sci. Inst.* **9,** 188, 230 (1938); **13,** 230 (1942)
J. D. Craggs, *Proc. Lond. Phys. Soc.* **9,** 137 (1942)
J. D. Craggs, *Nature*, **148,** 661 (1941)
J. D. Craggs and J. F. Smee, *Brit. J. Radiol* **15,** 228 (1942)
S. C. Curran and V. Petrzilka, *Proc. Camb. Phys. Soc.* **35,** 309 (1939)
S. C. Curran and J. E. Strothers, *Proc. Camb. Phil. Soc.* **35,** 654 (1939)
L. F. Curtiss, *Bur. of Stds. J. of Res.* **4,** 5, 115–123, 593, 601–608 (1930)
L. R. Cuykendall, *Rev. Sci. Inst.* **4,** 676 (1933)
W. E. Danforth and W. E. Ramsey, *Phys. Rev.* **49,** 854 (1936)
W. E. Danforth, *Phys. Rev.* **46,** 1026 (1934)
D. DeVault, *Rev. Sci. Inst.* **12,** 83 (1941)
W. U. Dittrich, *Phys.* **41,** 256–269 (1940)
G. F. VonDroste, *Zeits. f. Phys.* **100,** 529 (1936)
R. L. Driscoll, M. W. Hodge and A. Ruark, *Rev. Sci. Inst.* **11,** 241 (1940)
O. S. Duffendack and W. E. Morriss, *Rev. Sci. Inst.* **6,** 243 (1935)
O. S. Duffendack, H. Lipschutz and M. Slawsky, *Phys. Rev.* **52,** 1231 (1937)
J. Dunning and S. M. Skinner, *Rev. Sci. Inst.* **6,** 243 (1935)
J. V. Dunworth, *Rev. Sci. Inst.* **11,** 167 (1940)
A. Eisenstein and N. S. Gingrich, *Rev. Sci. Inst.* **12,** 582 (1941)
A. Eisenstein and N. S. Gingrich, *Phys. Rev.* **61,** 104 and 62, 296 (1942)
R. D. Evans and R. A. Mugele, *Rev. Sci. Inst.* **7,** 441 (1936)

R. D. Evans and R. L. Alder, *Rev. Sci. Inst.* **10,** 332 (1939)
R. D. Evans and R. E. Meagher, *Rev. Sci. Inst.* **10,** 339 (1939)
N. Feather and J. V. Dunworth, *Proc. Roy. Soc. A* **168,** 566 (1938)
H. Geiger, *Zeits. f. Phys.* **27,** 7 (1924)
J. Giarratana, *Rev. Sci. Inst.* **8,** 390 (1937)
H. Greinacher, *Zeits. f. Phys.* **23,** 371 (1924)
E. Greiner, *Zeits. f. Phys.* **81,** 543 (1933)
R. W. Gurney, *Proc. Roy. Soc. A* **107,** 332 (1925)
C. L. Haines, *Rev. Sci. Inst.* **7,** 411 (1936)
J. Halpern and O. C. Simpson, *Rev. Sci. Inst.* **8,** 172 (1937)
W. E. Hazen, *Phys. Rev.* **63,** 107 (1943)
A. von Hippel, *Zeits. f. Phys.* **97,** 455 (1936)
M. G. Holloway and M. S. Livingston, *Phys. Rev.* **54,** 18 (1936)
D. E. Hull, *Rev. Sci. Inst.* **11,** 404 (1940)
H. Hupperstberger, *Zeits. f. Phys.* **75,** 231 (1932)
R. Jaiger and J. Kluge, *Z. Instrumentchk* **52,** 229–232 (1932)
L. Janossy and R. Ingleby, *J. Sci. Inst.* **19,** 30–31 (1942)
Joneson, *Zeits. f. Phys.* **36,** 6, 426 (1926)
D. L. Jorgensen, *Rev. Sci. Inst.* **10,** 34 (1939)
O. W. Kenrick, *Electronics* **14,** 33–35, 74–76 (1941)
D. W. Kerst, *Rev. Sci. Inst.* **9,** 151 (1938)
W. Kolhorster and E. Weber, *Phys. Zeits.* **42,** 13 (1941)
S. A. Korff, *Phys. Rev.* **56,** 1241 (1939)
W. Kutzner, *Zeits. f. Phys.* **23,** 117 (1924)
L. M. Langer and R. T. Cox, *Rev. Sci. Inst.* **7,** 31 (1936)
D. P. LeGalley, *Rev. Sci. Inst.* **6,** 279 (1935)
W. F. Libby, D. D. Lee and S. Ruben, *Rev. Sci. Inst.* **8,** 38 (1937)
G. L. Locher, *J. Franklin Inst.* **216,** 553–556 (1933)
G. L. Locher and D. P. LeGalley, *Phys. Rev.* **46,** 1047 (1934)
G. L. Locher, *Phys. Rev.* **42,** 525 (1932); **50,** 1099 (1936)
L. B. Loeb, *Phys. Rev.* **48,** 684 (1935)
A. N. May, *Proc. Lond. Phys. Soc.* **51,** 26 (1939)
H. A. C. McKay, *Rev. Sci. Inst.* **12,** 103 (1941)
H. McMaster and M. L. Pool, *Rev. Sci. Inst.* **11,** 196 (1940)
G. Medicus, *Zeits. f. Phys.* **74,** 350 (1932)
G. Medicus, *Zeits. f. Phys.* **103,** 76 (1936)
C. G. Montgomery, D. B. Cowie, W. E. Ramsey and D. D. Montgomery, *Phys. Rev.* **56,** 635 (1939)
C. G. Montgomery, D. D. Montgomery, *J. Franklin Inst.* **229,** 585 (1940)
C. G. and D. D. Montgomery, *Phys. Rev.* **59,** 1045 (1941)

J. C. Mouzon, *Rev. Sci. Inst.* **7,** 467 (1936)
G. J. Neary, *Proc. Roy. Soc.* **175,** 71 (1940)
F. Norling, *Phys. Rev.* **58,** 277 (1940)
H. Paetow, *Zeits. f. Phys.* **111,** 770 (1939)
A. A. Petrankas and D. L. Northrup, *Rev. Sci. Inst.* **11,** 298 (1940)
W. E. Ramsey and M. R. Lipman, *Rev. Sci. Inst.* **6,** 121 (1935)
W. E. Ramsey, *Phys. Rev.* **58,** 1176 (1940)
W. E. Ramsey, E. Hudspeth and W. L. Lees, *Phys. Rev.* **59,** 685 (1941)
W. E. Ramsey and W. L. Lees, *Phys. Rev.* **60,** 411 (1941)
W. E. Ramsey and E. L. Hudspeth, *Phys. Rev.* **61,** 95–96 (1942)
W. E. Ramsey, *Phys. Rev.* **61,** 95–96 (1942)
W. E. Ramsey and W. E. Danforth, *Phys. Rev.* **51,** 1105 (1937)
H. J. Reich, *Rev. Sci. Inst.* **9,** 222 (1938)
A. Roberts, *Phys. Rev.* **57,** 564, 1069 (1940)
A. Roberts, *Rev. Sci. Inst.* **12,** 71 (1941)
G. D. Rochester and L. Janossy, *Phys. Rev.* **63,** 52 (1943)
M. E. Rose and W. E. Ramsey, *Phys. Rev.* **61,** 504–509 (1942)
E. Rutherford and H. Geiger, *Phil. Mag.* **24,** 618 (1912)
M. D. Santos, *Phys. Rev.* **62,** 178–179 (1942)
L. I. Schiff and A. D. Evans, *Rev. Sci. Inst.* **7,** 456 (1936)
J. Schintlmeister and W. Czulius, *Phys. Z.* **41,** 269–271 (1940)
J. E. Schrader, *Phys. Rev.* **6,** 292 (1915)
H. G. Stever, *Phys. Rev.* **59,** 765 (1941)
J. C. Street and R. H. Woodward, *Phys. Rev.* **56,** 1029 (1934)
H. M. Sullivan, *Rev. Sci. Inst.* **11,** 356 (1940)
W. F. Swann and G. L. Locher, *J. Franklin Inst.* **121,** 275 (1936)
R. B. Taft, *Rev. Sci. Inst.* **8,** 508 (1937)
R. B. Taft, *Rev. Sci. Inst.* **11,** 63 (1940)
J. Taylor, *Proc. Camb. Phil. Soc.* **24,** 251 (1928)
A. Trost, *Phys. Z.* **36,** 801 (1935)
J. A. Van Den Akker, *Rev. Sci. Inst.* **1,** 672 (1930)
E. Vickers and C. P. Saylor, *Rev. Sci. Inst.* **10,** 245 (1939)
J. C. Wang, J. F. Marvin and K. W. Stenstrom, *Rev. Sci. Inst.* **13,** 81 (1942)
E. Weber, *Phys. Z.,* **41,** 242–256 (1940)
H. C. Webster, *Proc. Camb. Phil. Soc.* **28,** 121–123 (1932)
P. Weisz, *Phys. Rev.* **61,** 392; **62,** 477 (1942)
P. Weisz and W. E. Ramsey, *Rev. Sci. Inst.* **13,** 258–264 (1942)
J. Zeleny, *Phys. Rev.* **24,** 255 (1924)

AUTHOR INDEX

SUBJECT INDEX

Charged Particles

+ | ← o | -

Determine mass
of by E.M. defl

Mass Spectrogr
weights atoms

April
All Science

Carbon (13) tracer
for Cancer Research
mass spectrograph u
to detect presence
in body.

Metastasis

"Committee on
Growth"

(Amer Ass for the Adv.
of Science 1848)

Franklin's
"Letters to a French

Man Real & Ideal
by E.G. CONKLIN
Zoologist

G.D. Birkhoff died 1937
mathmatician

Write
Wiley
Ray
Claire
Swindle
Notapoff
Fraser